An Illustrated History of Signalling

This page:
The interior of the MR signalbox at Ripley Junction photographed on 4 August 1926. At the end
of the box are two Tyer's No 6 single line tablet instruments and to their right two wire tensioners.
National Railway Museum (DY13982)

Following page:
The departure platforms at Paddington (GWR) in the closing years of the first decade of the 20th
century. *D. J. Powell Collection*

An Illustrated History of Signalling

Michael A. Vanns

IAN ALLAN
Publishing

Contents

First published 1997

ISBN 0 7110 2551 7

Published by Ian Allan Publishing

an imprint of Ian Allan Ltd, Terminal House, Station Approach, Shepperton, Surrey TW17 8AS.
Printed by Ian Allan Printing Ltd at its works at Coombelands in Runnymede, England.

Code: 9711/B

Front cover:
'A4' No 60006 *Sir Ralph Wedgwood* approaching Retford with a southbound express in the 1950s. *Derek Penney*

Back cover, top:
'Merchant Navy' class No 35012 *United States Lines* at Worting Junction in the final days of steam traction on the Southern Region. *Derek Penney*

Back cover, bottom:
The west end of Taunton station on 17 July 1985. As HST power-car No 43187 heads away from the camera, another London-bound service approaches under clear signals. All the signals were BR(WR) lower quadrant semaphores. *Author*

Right:
The first Cooke & Wheatstone electric telegraph instruments used on railways were connected by cables at ground level but from the mid-1840s until the 1970s, overhead cables and the 'pole route' were familiar features along every railway line. Wiring the routes was a science all of its own; whole treatises were written on how to attach the cables to the insulators, how to solder the joints and exactly how much 'sag' the cables had to have between each pole. The actual job of maintaining the pole route called for a certain degree of nerve as well as technical knowledge, however, as this 1950s photograph of a BR(LM) lineman clearly shows. *BR(LMR)*

Foreword

Following the author's first book on the subject — *abc Signalling in the Age of Steam* (Ian Allan Ltd 1995) — it was a great privilege to be given the opportunity by the publishers to expand on that text, add more illustrations, and produce the result as a large format volume.

In many ways, the two books complement each other, an understanding of the basic procedures and regulations as outlined in the abc being a useful preamble to the *Illustrated History*. In *abc Signalling in the Age of Steam* the emphasis is on the traditional, the typical and the fundamental procedures and equipment that kept the majority of trains running safely in the period 1830 to 1968. The strength of this latest book is that it aims to tell the whole story of signalling from 1830 through to privatisation in 1994. It addresses all those subjects not covered in the *abc* and attempts to put them into an historical context.

As well as the early history leading to the emergence of 'traditional' signalling methods and equipment in the later half of the 19th century, this volume examines the experiments with 'power signalling' in the two decades before World War 1, looks at the development of colour-light signalling during the interwar period, the emergence of power signalboxes in the late 1950s, their evolution into signalling centres in the following two decades, and finally charts the amazing advances made possible by the use of computer technology from the mid-1980s onwards. The text is detailed, but the book is not intended to be a technical one nor a procedures manual; its aim is to be a new history of signalling.

This has not been easy. While writing the text, a group of dedicated experts supported by the Friends of the National Railway Museum have been painstakingly compiling what it is hoped will be the definitive, academic history of signalling. Their efforts remind you how difficult it is to be a solo historian these days, the present author being no O. S. Nock. Naturally this history is biased towards those elements the author considers important and interesting, and what he believes forms a coherent story. Inevitably there are a number of topics that have not been included, or have not been covered in the detail they deserve. If they had, the text would probably have become twice as long as it is now. Signalling on 'underground' and industrial railways is not covered, nor is the history of Irish signalling. Another casualty has been the story of 'train control', introduced on a number of mainland railways just before World War 1 to improve efficiency and the economical use of locomotives and crews, and control more logically the pathing of goods trains between ever more frequent and rapid passenger services. It was the need to co-ordinate the work of thousands of individual signalboxes that inspired progressive signal engineers in the 1930s to develop ways of controlling larger areas from single signalboxes, their ideas leading directly to the powerboxes of the 1960s, paving the way to the signalling centres of the 1970s, and the ultimate in train control: the present day 'Integrated Electronic Control Centres' (IECCs).

The author has not been able to discuss in depth the social history of signalling either. There has been no room to mention signalling schools, nor the training of signalmen and S&T (Signal & Telegraph) staff. Working practices, working conditions, hours, pay, the disruption to working routines during resignalling projects and the effects of the large number of redundancies resulting from modernisation schemes particularly in the last 50 years deserve detailed studies of their own. But because the human dimension in this book is secondary to the technical developments, this does not imply the author considers it less important or less significant. Not only is he no O. S. Nock, the author is no Adrian Vaughan either.

Nevertheless, there is more than enough here to satisfy those who work within the industry, the knowledgeable reader and the ubiquitous 'man in the street'. A good history should illuminate past events, not just chronicle them, and the present author hopes this work is more than a chronicle of signalling developments over the last 165 years.

Michael A. Vanns
Coalbrookdale
Summer 1997

Abbreviations

BR(E)	British Rail, Eastern Region
BR(LM)	British Rail, London Midland Region
BR(NE)	British Rail, North Eastern Region
BR(Sc)	British Rail, Scottish Region
BR(S)	British Rail, Southern Region
BR(W)	British Rail, Western Region
CLC	Cheshire Lines Committee
CR	Caledonian Railway
FR	Furness Railway
GCR	Great Central Railway
GER	Great Eastern Railway
GJR	Grand Junction Railway
GNSR	Great North of Scotland Railway
GNR	Great Northern Railway
GSWR	Glasgow & South Western Railway
GWR	Great Western Railway
HR	Highland Railway
L&BR	London & Birmingham Railway
LBSCR	London, Brighton & South Coast Railway
LCDR	London, Chatham & Dover Railway
LDECR	Lancashire, Derbyshire & East Coast Railway
L&MR	Liverpool & Manchester Railway
LMS	London, Midland & Scottish Railway
LNER	London & North Eastern Railway
LNW/GWJ	London & North Western & Great Western Joint Railway
LNWR	London & North Western Railway
LSWR	London & South Western Railway
LTSR	London, Tilbury & Southend Railway
L&YR	Lancashire & Yorkshire Railway
M&GN	Midland & Great Northern Joint Railway
MR	Midland Railway
MSLR	Manchester, Sheffield & Lincolnshire Railway
NBR	North British Railway
NER	North Eastern Railway
NLR	North London Railway
NSR	North Staffordshire Railway
S&DJ	Somerset & Dorset Joint Railway
SECR	South Eastern & Chatham Railway
SER	South Eastern Railway
SR	Southern Railway

Dedication

This book is dedicated to my uncle and all the signalmen I knew in and around Newark-on-Trent, who in the dying days of mechanical signalling kindled an interest for me that will never be extinguished.

Acknowledgements

The author would like to thank the following who helped in the preparation of this book (with apologies to anyone who has been omitted): Reg Instone, Research Co-ordinator of the Signalling Record Society, for reading through and correcting the text; John Powell, Librarian of the Ironbridge Gorge Museum, for allowing the author unlimited access to the Transport Trust Library; David Houlston for once again producing quality prints from the author's negatives; Donald Powell for allowing the author to go through his entire photographic collection and use any image that was relevant; Gerry Arundel of the Historical Model Railway Society, for allowing the author to hunt through the society's photographic archive and for printing up the chosen images; Alan Whitaker, Communications Manager of Railtrack LNE and Signalling Manager, Joe Williams, for making my visit to York IECC not only possible but informative; Steve Fountain, of Fastline Photographic, York; Ed Bartholomew, Curator of the National Railway Museum's Photographic Collection; Eddie Johnson; Jeffrey Sankey of The Sankey Collection; A. E. W. Colbourn; S. J. Duffell; Peter Waller; the staff of Birmingham Central Library; and finally, the local studies librarians at Dover Library (Mrs Godfrey), Mansfield Library (Mr Crute), Carlisle Library (Mr Foster), Newcastle upon Tyne Library (Mr Thurston), The Mitchell Library, Glasgow (Mr Gordon), and Guildford Library (Ms Fenton).

'It is a trite axiom, that two solid bodies cannot occupy the same space at the same time. The duty of the railway signalling engineer may be said to be to endeavour to prevent two bodies, which are moving at high velocities, from seeking to violate this law of nature.'
(Richard Christopher Rapier, Assoc Inst CE, 31 March 1874)

Left:
This is an example of one of the GWR's earliest standard signalbox designs, used from the very end of the 1860s until about 1875. Milton Crossing was on the main line just outside Didcot. The photograph dates from just before World War 1. *Author's Collection*

Right:
The LNWR signalman at Harrow completing entries in the train register in October of 1905. *National Railway Museum (LMS 815)*

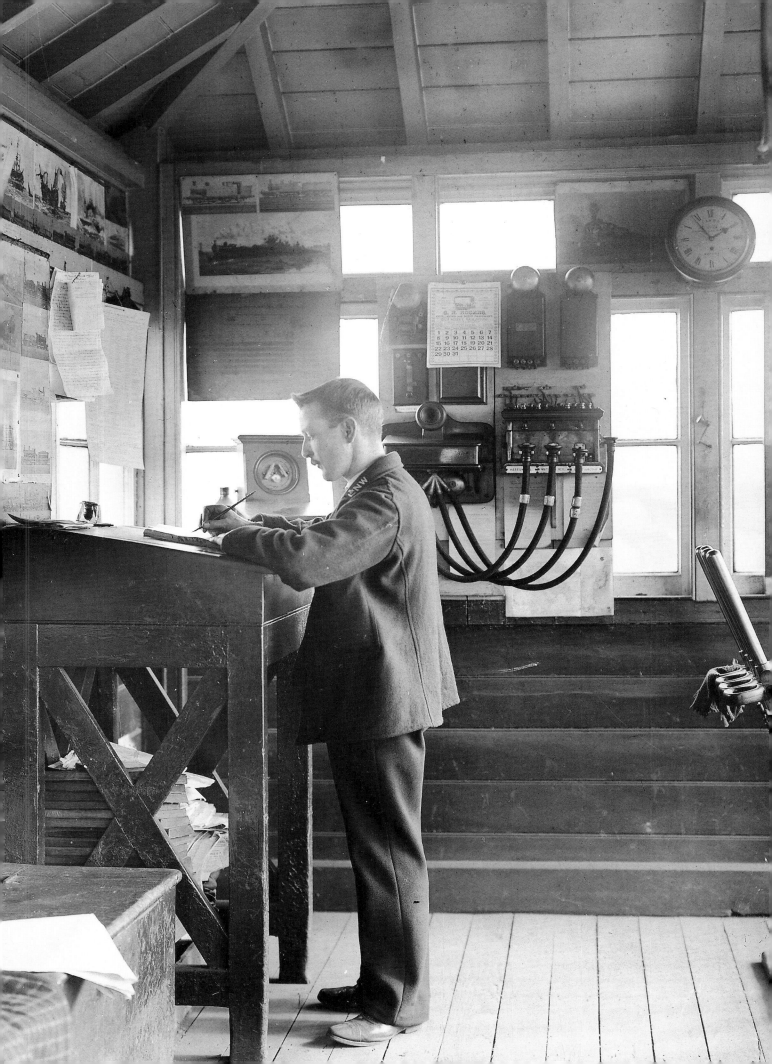

1 The Early Years 1830-50

At the beginning of the 1830s travelling by railway was an adventure. But it was a restricted adventure. Most of the country was not within reach of a railway line, and where there was access, travelling by train was expensive. For first class ticket holders a journey by rail was quicker than travelling by stage coach but trains were not fast; a trip of 31 miles between Liverpool and Manchester in 1832, for example, took 1½hr by the fastest train, at an average of 20mph. Trains were not very frequent either and few travelled at night.

At the end of the decade it was possible to travel from either Liverpool or Manchester to London by train in far less time than it had taken by the fastest stage coach. But it was still a long journey by the limited number of trains available. At the beginning of 1839, a journey between London and Birmingham by the fastest of seven trains (Monday to Saturday), took 6hr, at an average speed of 18mph. By the end of the year, two extra weekday through trains had been added to the timetable, their timings cut by half an hour, which pushed the average speed to 20mph.

In 1842 the recently opened London & Brighton Railway ran only eight trains each way over its line, Mondays to Saturdays, with just three on Sundays. There were only two night trains: the 10pm goods from London Bridge station which arrived at Brighton at 1.30 in the morning, and the 8pm mixed passenger and goods train from Brighton, arriving in London at 10.30pm. The fastest trains (two each day in either direction) averaged 25mph.

By the end of the 1840s the situation was completely different. Almost everyone had access to rail travel. Almost every major town had a railway connection, and if not it was either under construction or was planned. Local coaches and carriers had altered their routes to reach the nearest railhead and many more trains operated, every company obliged by Act of Parliament to run at least one train a day each way charging no more than 1d a mile. Although these trains were some of the slowest on the line, most others were considerably faster than 20 years before. In 1845 the GWR ran a Paddington to Exeter express (later named the 'Flying Dutchman') at an average speed of 44mph. At the beginning of the decade the fastest speed achieved by a train on the LSWR was just over 25mph; by the end of the decade it had risen to 44½mph.

The Time Interval System

In the first few years of the 1830s, therefore, controlling trains was well within the capabilities of a driver and fireman keeping a good eye on the track in front of them. A policeman at the lineside with a flag and a few arm gestures helped to reassure the passengers. But as the frequency of trains increased as the decade progressed, tighter control was required.

The Liverpool & Manchester Railway was the first company to regulate its trains using the 'time interval system'. The railway policemen employed at passenger stations, among their other tasks, had to make sure that a certain time elapsed after a train had departed before another could follow it on the same track. During this time they had to show a red flag, or a red light at night. Once that period had passed, they could display a green 'caution' flag or a green light to any following train, which indicated to the driver to be on the look out for a preceding train. A few more minutes after the cautionary period and the line was considered clear again, and a white flag could be displayed, or a white light at night. By the end of the decade most railways had adopted this system and in January 1841 at a meeting of a number of companies, it was agreed that the colours used by the L&MR to indicate danger (red), caution (green) and all clear (white) should become the standard.

Over the years, the interval of time between each signal was varied by the companies using the system. When the capacity of a line had to be increased, the intervals were simply reduced. In the Edinburgh & Glasgow Railway's Rules & Regulations book of January 1842, for example, the danger signal was displayed for 15min after a passenger train had passed, and 10min if a luggage train. In the NSR's Rules & Regulations book of March 1848, the interval between the display of a danger and caution signal was only 5min, with caution being displayed for a further 5min before the line was again considered to be clear.

Flags to Boards

In the early 1830s almost every train stopped at every station and, therefore, policemen holding coloured flags during the day and lamps at night could not have been too difficult for engine drivers to spot. But inevitably as speeds gradually increased, it became more important for drivers to be able to see signals from as far away as possible, particularly when approaching junctions where they might not be expected to stop and where the risk of collision was greater than elsewhere. Engravings of the Grand Junction Railway when that first opened in 1837, show flags hoisted on very tall poles, and these became known as 'permanent', 'stationary' or 'fixed' signals.

It is said that the L&MR was the first company to erect a fixed signal — a post with a lantern on top for displaying a light at night — and very soon variously shaped boards superseded flags as day-time fixed signals. It is claimed that the GJR used semi-circular board signals from its opening, but none appear on the early engravings already referred to.

In the 1840s the number of board signals in use increased, as did their variety, and soon there were almost as many differently shaped boards as there were railway companies using them. Some boards were completely circular — usually referred to as 'discs', others were triangular, others square (Pictures 1 & 2). Whatever their design, all were made so they could be rotated through 90° about a vertical axis. When policemen wanted to indicate danger, they turned the board on to face the driver, and when they wanted to indicate that the line was clear, they turned the board off so that the driver could not see it. This terminology passed into general use and remains so today; when a signal shows danger it is considered to be in the 'on' position, and when at all clear it is said to be 'off'. At night lamps capable of displaying two or three colours were used. Whether these supplemented the board indications or were used instead of them at night is unclear.

The disadvantage with board signals was that they could only display two positive indications — one face of the board painted red for danger, the other side green for caution. The third all clear indication was a completely negative one — ie the board turned edge-on so that the driver could not see it. 'No signal = all clear' was of course a recipe for disaster. This fundamental defect was properly addressed only by the GWR, the first of a new generation of railway, planned and built for speed. Shortly after its main line between London and Bristol had opened throughout in 1841, the company began to erect the first of its famous 'disc and crossbar' signals. A circular disc was positioned above a rectangular board and set at 90° to it. When the disc was displayed it signified all clear — a positive and unmistakable indication — and when the disc was rotated edge-on to the track the crossbar became visible, indicating danger — 'stop' (Picture 3).

That still left the problem of the caution indication. This was displayed using a separate board signal shaped like an arrow, positioned beneath the disc and crossbar or separate from it. When it pointed away from the track with its green side facing the approaching train, it signified caution; when it was turned edge-on to the driver and could not be seen, he then relied on the indication of the main disc and crossbar; when the arrow was swung towards the track and its red side

1840s the firm went into production with this new piece of signalling equipment. The most popular form of the signal was one with two arms for controlling trains at double track stations and because of this it soon became known as the 'station semaphore' (Picture 5). Some of the earliest examples had arms with a number of slots cut into them, presumably to reduce wind resistance. One of the first of this pattern was installed at London Bridge station, and W. E. Edwards, writing in the Railway Magazine of 1905, believed it was probably the first erected at a London terminus.

Stevens & Sons continued to develop the semaphore and in 1847 James Stevens of the firm patented a mechanism (No 11612) incorporating a bevel gear arrangement so that the signal lamp and the semaphore arm were moved simultaneously by the same handle at the base of the post. The LNWR Rules of 1849 make it clear that that railway company was using such semaphores by then. In the same patent specification, Stevens also introduced a counter-weight to the rod linking the handle to the arm, so that if the handle slipped, the arm was automatically pulled to the danger position. This was probably the first application of the principle of 'fail-safe', which became of paramount importance in all subsequent equipment design. Unfortunately, although Stevens' idea was sound, the actual mechanism had a fundamental flaw, because if the arm became disconnected from the rod, the arm dropped to all clear. It was not until the 1860s that the arrangement was altered so the semaphore arm was pushed to all clear, eliminating the potential danger.

was displayed, the indication was danger. By the 1850s this arrow-shaped or fantail board was often used on its own as a station signal (Picture 4).

Boards to Semaphores

Disc and crossbar signals were probably the most effective of the early fixed signals and were used by the Bristol & Exeter, Somerset & Dorset, North Devon, South Devon, Furness and London & North Western railways. The GWR continued to use its disc and crossbar signals into the 1870s, but some other simpler board signals were even longer-lasting. The Scottish railways were some of the last railway companies in this country to use such signals, the NBR 'vane' types being very ornate and mounted on elegant cast-iron posts.

But long before then a much neater solution to the problem of displaying three indications with just one signal had been achieved. At the very end of 1841, C. H. Gregory, Engineer of the London & Croydon Railway, erected the first railway semaphore signal at New Cross. Semaphores were already used by the Admiralty to send messages over land — the Semaphore Telegraph — so Gregory only put existing technology to a different use. But the achievement was not in the use of the semaphore itself but in the codification of just three of the possible positions the arm could assume in relation to its post. Gregory chose to make those indications in the lower left-hand quadrant. When the arm was at 90° to the post it indicated danger, when the arm was inclined downwards at 45° it indicated caution, and when it was out of sight in a slot in the post it indicated all clear. At night when the arm was invisible, lamps capable of displaying three colours continued in use. It should be remembered that these lamps were lit only at night. Day-time and night-time signals were still perceived as completely different. Even though the semaphore arm and lamp were usually attached to the same post, the action of moving the former had no effect on the lamp, which on the first semaphore signals was operated from a separate handle.

Gregory's semaphore was made for him by Stevens & Sons of Darlington Works, Southwark Bridge Road, London, and in the

Auxiliaries, Distants and Detonators

Improving the mechanism of the station semaphore and making its signal more visible for drivers was one development of the 1840s, and another was the provision of an additional signal placed a few hundred yards before the station signal — in later railway language, in rear of it. This auxiliary or 'distant' signal was intended to give drivers advance warning of what the main station semaphore was indicating.

The use of the extra signal varied between companies but normally the auxiliary showed no indication if the station signal was displaying all clear or caution, and was only 'turned on' if the station signal showed danger. Auxiliaries were consequently only two-position signals. They were also the first signals to be operated by wires from levers

Above (4):
The double track broad gauge lines at Newport station photographed at the beginning of the 1870s. On the right, the red side of the arrow-shaped or fantail board is facing the camera, indicating danger.
S. J. Duffell Collection

Below (5):
A double arm station semaphore signal on the Festiniog Railway. Although this particular example was used on a Welsh narrow gauge mineral line, it is nevertheless typical of what was in use on many main lines in the 1850s.
Real Photographs

next to the main station signal, some rule books of the period actually referring to them as 'wire signals' *(Picture 6)*. Sometimes two wires were used, one to pull the signal to danger, the other to pull it back to all clear, but it was not long before counter-weights were added.

For many years after semaphores had become the most common signal at stations, auxiliaries continued to be variously shaped boards *(Picture 7)*, one of the few exceptions being on the GNR which used semaphores exclusively for all its main line signals in the 1850s.

It seems that the way the auxiliary was used varied in the years before 'block working' replaced the time interval system (see next chapter). The 1849 LNWR Rules & Regulations book had this to say about the signals:

'These Auxiliary Signals are intended to warn the Engineman and Guards in thick weather (when the main Signal cannot be well seen at the usual distance) of the RED being turned on at the Station, and for this purpose a GREEN Signal is shown at the Auxiliary Post. Except when the Red Signal is shown at the Station, no Signal whatever is shown by the Auxiliary.'

There was no mention of drivers having to stop at the auxiliary, but this was specifically mentioned in Rule 78 of the Eastern Counties Railway's Rules & Regulations book of September 1854:

'Should a train arrive before the line is clear, it must be brought to a stand outside the Auxiliary Post, after which the Signal must be lowered to allow the Train to pass within its protection, and then be placed again at *Danger* and remain so whilst the Train is at, and until it has got clear away from, the Station.'

According to the GNR Rules & Regulations book of 1855 (revised 1867), drivers had to bring their trains under control if the distant was in the 'on' position, but if they could see the line was all clear they were authorized to pass it at 5mph.

Whatever the operating practices of the various companies, it must be assumed that although the term 'auxiliary' and 'distant' seem to have been interchangeable, the way these signals were used was not the same as

distant signals in block working of the 1870s (see next chapter).

It is also interesting to glean from the early rule books that auxiliary signals were seen by some companies as a way of protecting stationary trains without the need for the guard to go back and put detonators on the line. This was certainly the case on the Eastern Counties Railway in the mid-1850s. Detonators, or 'audible' signals, were developed by E. A. Cowper in 1844 and their use was very soon being recommended by the Railway Inspectorate of the Board of Trade.

As early as 1839, the L&MR's Rule Book required guards of trains stopped during foggy weather to go back 400yd to warn other approaching trains. Over the years other railways adopted this rule and when detonators became available, instructions were given to place these at intervals along the line behind stationary trains. The NSR's Rules & Regulations of 1848 were very detailed about the use of detonators to protect trains, 12 detonators being issued as standard equipment to guards, policemen, switchmen, enginemen, gatemen, foremen and gangers and station clerks. The manufacture of detonators became an important industry, Kynoch & Co of Birmingham (well known in the late Victorian period for its sporting and small-arm ammunition) producing almost 300,000 per week.

Stirrups and Levers

After successfully introducing the semaphore to railway operation, Gregory remained in the forefront of signalling developments, when in 1844 at Bricklayers Arms Junction just south of London Bridge station he provided a raised platform on which two double arm semaphores were mounted and operated from a frame of stirrups, alongside the two point levers. The new mechanism was made by Stevens & Sons *(Picture 8)*.

As had become standard practice at junctions, all the arms remained in the danger position until one had to be lowered to the caution position to allow a train over the points. But the innovation was in the stirrup mechanism. Once one arm had been lowered, another that might signal a conflicting route could not be moved because the stirrup operating it was physically prevented from moving by the position of the one that had already been depressed. The point levers were not connected in a similar way but nevertheless the mechanism was the first positive piece of 'interlocking' and Stevens & Sons went into production with it. As already mentioned above, in James Stevens' 1847 patent, counter-weights were shown attached to the rod operating semaphores and in the same patent it is specifically noted that because of this, signalmen had to keep their foot on the stirrup to maintain the signal at 'line clear', otherwise it returned automatically to danger.

Above (6):
Sutton Coldfield station c1867. At the base of the station semaphore post, the handle for holding the arm in one of three positions can be clearly seen. Next to it, between the post and the ladder, is the weighted lever to operate the auxiliary or distant signal.
Author's Collection

Policemen to Signalmen

By 1850, when all these clever devices were finding limited acceptance on the country's railways, the policemen of the previous decades had themselves evolved into signalmen and pointsmen, a special class of railway worker usually overworked and underpaid, whose specific job was the manipulation of semaphores, boards and points.

In the period covered by this chapter, signalmen did not yet have the status accorded to their class in later years. It appears that many were still illiterate, and even if this was not the case, there was an assumption on the part of management that they were of limited ability. One common prejudice against the introduction of more complex pieces of signalling machinery, was the belief that they were beyond the wit of signalmen and pointsmen to operate competently. It was also claimed that new mechanical devices would make the men — and engine drivers — more complacent about their work. As late as 1873 at an Institution of Civil Engineers meeting, it was still possible to make the following comment about signalmen:

'They should be men of a peculiar class, who thought practically of nothing but signalling. A genius or an intelligent man might be wandering when he ought to be looking at his signal.'

It is hardly surprising, therefore, that in the period 1830-50, signalmen were not trusted with the use of what was probably the most important innovation of this early period in railway history — the electric telegraph.

The Electric Telegraph

The principles stretched back into the 18th century, but it was not until William Cooke and Charles Wheatstone formed a partnership in 1837 and took out a patent that same year (No 7390), that the transmission of messages over long distances by electricity became a practical proposition. Robert Stephenson, engineer of the London & Birmingham Railway then nearing completion, was particularly enthusiastic about the electric telegraph and allowed Cooke to install two five-needle instruments to communicate between Euston station and the engine house at Camden Town. The demonstration was entirely satisfactory, but Stephenson was unable to convince the L&BR directors to install the system permanently, and the credit for this went to I. K. Brunel and the GWR. The two instruments were once again pressed into use, this time at Paddington and West Drayton, and the circuit was operational by July 1839.

The GWR system was immediately successful but it was still perceived as something of a curiosity, as little more than a clever experiment. Cooke, however, was very keen to promote the electric telegraph as a practical and useful installation, and in 1840 he was given the opportunity to install a circuit on the London & Blackwall Railway. The original five-needle instruments were impressive pieces of carpentry and instrument making, but Cooke abandoned all this elaboration and installed at each station instruments with just one needle, their indications repeated at the London engine house on one instrument with five needles.

When the needle was deflected to one side it indicated 'ready', and to the other it indicated 'stop'. Because steam locomotives were not used on the line and the passenger carriages were attached to and detached from a continuous rope, the electric telegraph was the only way of transmitting instructions to the engine house at London. It was the very first electric telegraph installation used to control the movement of trains between stations.

In the GWR system a number of needles deflecting in relation to each other had to be read in sequence to build up a complete message, but what was significant about the Blackwall system was that each needle could be pointed to a full message — ie 'Ready' or 'Stop'. The way in which the GWR instruments were used made them the direct precursors of the 'speaking telegraph' instruments of the next decade, usually containing just one or sometimes two needles, which were deflected from side to side to spell out a message (eventually using the Morse Code; left = dot, right = dash). The way in which the Blackwall instruments were used made them the direct ancestors of 'block telegraph' instruments (see next chapter).

The London & Blackwall Railway was a very short commuter line and by the time it was fully operational in 1841, it was possible to travel far greater distances behind steam locomotives: from London to Birmingham, Brighton, Bristol, Southampton and York. But steam traction was not yet the unquestioned means of moving trains about. Brunel would not have convinced the directors of the South Devon Railway to adopt atmospheric traction if he had not believed it would work. He was also convinced for very practical reasons that track laid to his broad gauge (7ft) was superior to Stephenson's 'narrow' gauge (4ft 8½in). In the early 1840s, before the Gauge Commissioners decided the latter should become the 'standard' gauge, and before the Railway Mania set the standards for all future railway development, there was still the opportunity for lively debate about most aspects of railway construction and operation. There were all manner of fanciful ideas, including Cooke's proposal to control the passage of trains along single tracks using the electric telegraph. But his ideas were no more or less far-fetched than Brunel's belief in atmospheric traction. Only with hindsight is it possible to say that atmospheric traction was a failure, whereas Cooke's ideas created the foundations of modern signalling practice.

Telegraphic Railways

In 1842 Cooke published a book entitled *Telegraphic Railways*. Basing his theories on the practical experience of running the London & Blackwall line, he suggested dividing up single lines into 'Grand Divisions' of between 15 and 25 miles long with principal stations at either end, and then further subdividing these into 'Stages' of between two and five miles long. Every stage

was to have a telegraph instrument capable of showing the indications of every other stage, while at the principal stations at either end of the Grand Division, instruments would display the indications of all the intermediate instruments. The normal position of each needle was to be upright, and when inclined to the left or right would indicate whether a train was approaching in the up or down direction. Obviously, when the needle showed that a train was travelling in the up direction, a railway policeman knew he could not send a train in the down direction. Cooke's theory, although formulated for the operation of just single lines, could be applied to the regulation of trains on double track, the telegraph providing the only practical means of ensuring that an interval of space instead of time was maintained between trains. In the following decade his ideas formed the basis of the 'block system' (see next chapter).

It is difficult to tell how influential Cooke's ideas were when he published them. It is probably true to say that most railway

managers were more concerned with buying locomotives powerful and reliable enough to maintain their published timetables and pull the increasing tonnage of freight traffic, than with worrying about the operation of delicate electrical instruments. In 1843 the GWR extended the telegraph from West Drayton to Slough, taking the opportunity to replace the original five-needle instruments with more up-to-date two-needle versions. But the installation was still something of a novelty, with the public charged to see 'the wonder of the age!'. It was used only for sending messages and not for controlling trains, and the former became the traditional role associated with the electric telegraph until the invention of the telephone. When the Electric Telegraph Company, with Cooke as a director, was formed in 1845, it certainly made its money by installing telegraph wires along the thousands of miles of new railway created during the Railway Mania years, but the circuits were used for everything but the regulation of train movements.

Above (8):
The junction semaphores worked from the stirrup frame just visible on the platform at Bricklayers Arms Junction. The policeman has his right hand on one of the two point levers. An engraving from the *Illustrated London News*, December 1844.
Reproduced by permission of Birmingham Library Service

That development had to wait until the next decade. Until then Cooke's theories outlined in *Telegraphic Railways* were, as he advocated, put into practice on single track railways, beginning with the Norwich & Yarmouth Railway which opened in 1844, and followed a few months later by the SER on its single line between Tonbridge and Maidstone. By the end of the 1840s, the only other railway locations where the telegraph was used to control the movement of trains were through tunnels with either single or double track.

2 The Patent Years 1850-89

Between 1850 and 1889, the number of miles of railway line open in Great Britain increased by over 150%, an expansion never matched before or since. This alone makes the achievement of providing comprehensive signalling for almost all of the 10,000 miles opened to traffic in this period even more impressive. As the network grew, there were more inventions and patents for railway equipment than at any other time in railway history. Some were useful, others not. Some were development cul-de-sacs, but many more helped to create the solid foundations for railway operation as we would recognise it today.

By the end of the 1860s the railways were poised to enter a new era by exploiting all the best developments that had gone before. What followed in the 1870s was a minor revolution based on the fusion of four vital elements. The first was the acceptance of the principle of maintaining an interval of space, not time, between trains running on the same track — the 'block system'. The other three were the creation of the fully interlocked lever frame, the patenting of a number of purpose-designed 'block instruments', and the combined use of these last two elements in purpose-built signalboxes. After the 1870s, the way in which railways were operated became surprisingly standardised, and the standards established in the years covered by this chapter were used to keep the trains running safely for the next 100 years (*Pictures 9 & 10*).

In the 1850s the railway companies were still largely pioneers of a growing industry, not fully in control of the technology; after the 1870s they believed they had that industry under control, with a place for everything and everybody, and everything and everybody in its place. At last signalling — the block system, interlocking and the rigorous implementation of Rules & Regulations — played a crucial role in keeping this great railway machine functioning safely and profitably.

By 1889 the majority of the country's railways were safer than ever before, because of the comprehensive signalling systems installed in the previous 20 years. The horror of the Armagh disaster in June that year, which led to the Regulation of Railways Act 1889, was real and the legislation was appropriate, forcing all railway companies:
(i) to provide interlocking on lines used by passenger traffic;
(ii) to install continuous automatic brakes on all passenger trains;
(iii) to control the journeys of all those trains using the Absolute Block System.

But in reality the battle for all these requirements had already been won.

1850-60
The Block System

At the start of this decade, signalling was no longer a novelty, but those who wished to make innovations and improve procedures still had a fight with many railway managers, who tended to see greater reliance on signalling as a hindrance to their business aims.

In the 1840s the electric telegraph had proved useful for business; there was money to be made out of allowing the Electric Telegraph Co to install wires at the side of railway lines and by charging people to send messages. But it was also obvious that the potential for accidents to happen in tunnels and on single lines could be reduced (and compensation bills avoided) if the telegraph was used to actually control the passage of trains through these high risk sections. Consequently, the electric telegraph had become the accepted way of operating trains through tunnels and over single lines in the 1840s. The breakthrough of the 1850s was the use of this 'block system' by a number of railway companies on their double track main lines.

For the system to work properly, or 'absolutely', only one train at a time going in the same direction was allowed to occupy a section or block of track, the entrance to and exit from it being controlled by signalmen.

One of the first companies to replace time interval working with block working was the SER. In 1851, Charles Vincent Walker, the company's Telegraph Superintendent, installed 'single-stroke' bells at Spa Road and London Bridge station so that the signalmen at those two places could inform each other what trains were leaving and approaching the terminus. The system was put into use between 22 and 31 January 1852. Gradually, a whole network of bells was created, so that by the beginning of the 1860s it extended over 275 miles of track. By exchanging coded messages made up of a certain number and combination of beats on the bell, signalmen could establish whether an up or down train was due, and whether the line between stations was unobstructed for its journey. No train was allowed to leave a station until the signalman at the station where the train was to travel to had confirmed that the line was clear. Every code sent had to be repeated by the receiving signalman, both men recording the exchange of codes in what later became known as the train register. At every level crossing, bells were attached to the circuit wires, so that crossing keepers also heard the codes.

In 1854 Walker devised an instrument which could be used in addition to the bells. This was called the 'Semaphore Electric Telegraph', because instead of a single, centrally-pivoted needle which had been the key visual element in telegraph instruments since Cooke & Wheatstone's patent in 1837, Walker used a miniature semaphore arm. The idea was that it should effectively tell a signalman what indications his outdoor signals should display. When a signalman operated a handle, the miniature arm was raised or lowered to indicate either danger or all clear, and these indications were transmitted to, and repeated on, the instrument at the other end of the section. According to Walker himself, the instrument was constructed as an experiment and no more than one pair was ever put into use in the 1850s. But in the following decade others were made and used, some with finely carved cabinets with gothic details. The 1854 instrument was not patented, but when Walker's single-stroke bell and miniature semaphores were later combined in one case, the electrical and mechanical mechanism for moving the semaphores and sounding the bell was patented by C. V. & A. O. Walker in 1865 (No 488).

It was claimed in the 1850s that the SER was able to operate its lines using the block system because traffic was light, regular and passenger stations not too far apart. The NLR was also able to implement the block system, as its passenger stations were closely spaced, but on lines where stations were more than two miles apart, where there were intermediate sidings and when traffic became more intense, the idea of allowing only one train at a time between stations was obviously seen as a hindrance to the traffic flow. The solution was to divide that distance up further, by establishing special 'signal stations' manned solely by signalmen with semaphores and access to single-stroke bells or the electric telegraph. But it was the additional expenditure of building these signal stations that was used as an excuse by some companies for not adopting the block system. On the LNWR in the 1850s, however, the erection and manning of signal stations was found to be a cheaper alternative than laying extra track for the increasing number of trains travelling between London and Rugby, and so the company adopted the block system as an economy measure.

For controlling the LNWR's system, Edwin Clark, Chief Engineer of the Electric Telegraph Co, recommended using modified telegraph instruments with two separate, centrally-pivoted vertical needles, one for the up line and one for the down. Each instrument had two handles which, like their telegraph counterparts, when moved to the right or left activated the electrical circuit for each needle. By pointing the needle to one side 'line clear' could be indicated, and to the other 'train on line'. Unlike their telegraph ancestors, metal pegs attached to the instruments by short chains were used to keep the handles in the appropriate position, giving rise to the term 'pegging instrument', or in signalman's slang, 'pegger'. C. V. Walker claimed the term 'block', as in 'block working', originated from such instruments that could be pegged or blocked to give a permanent indication.

Normally the handles were held over to the left, thereby allowing current to continue to flow through the coils maintaining the needles at line clear. When trains passed between the signal stations, the handles at both stations were moved to the right so that the needle indicated train on line. If a train ran into trouble out of sight of a signal station, train crews were instructed to cut through the telegraph wires, which of course meant that the instrument needles dropped by gravity to an intermediate position between line clear and train on line — 'line blocked'. This terminology was to become the standard for all subsequent block instruments, although the usage changed subtly. Work on dividing up the stretch of line between London and Rugby into 'block sections' of approximately two miles in length began in 1855 and the system was christened 'Clark's Two Mile Telegraph'.

At the same time, the LNWR's great rival the GNR was also bringing the block system into use on its main line out of London. In March 1851 the Electric Telegraph Co had the telegraph working as far as Doncaster and in April it was extended to York. Time interval working was in operation between stations, but in the tunnels between London and Hatfield the telegraph enabled trains to be worked through using the block system. In 1854, Edwin Clark recommended that the whole of this stretch of line could be so worked and this is just what the GNR did, with further installations at Doncaster and in 1856 between Hatfield and Hitchin. It appears that the GNR used very similar double-needle instruments to those on the LNWR, but without the ability to 'peg' the indications.

At the end of the 1850s, the L&YR joined the list of companies using the absolute block system when it installed 185 new telegraph instruments on its lines. These were described as Highton's semaphore variety in an article which appeared in the 16 September 1859 edition of *The Engineer*. (The term semaphore is probably misleading, as a description of the first Highton instrument of 1854 implies it used a disc to display the indication.) Installation on the L&YR had taken five months and an interesting feature of the system was the telegraphing of 'Greenwich time' from Hunts Bank (Victoria) station, Manchester, to every station each morning at 10 o'clock. Many generations of signalmen were to become familiar with that ritual and the careful correcting of their signalbox clocks.

Platforms to Signalboxes

In the 1860s, and especially the 1870s, telegraph and block instruments and the mechanisms for working the signals and points would have been located in purpose-built signalboxes. But this was not the case until the very end of the 1850s. Almost no photographs survive of the sort of structures the LNWR, GNR and L&YR were using for signalling purposes in the 1850s, although the buildings used by the SER which do appear in early photographs probably date from this period. Huts, timber or brick, to shelter railway policemen, pointsmen and/or signalmen were not an unusual feature at stations and junctions in the 1850s, but they did not contain any of the mechanisms for operating the signals and points. It was the patenting of John Saxby's 'simultaneous motion' frame in 1856 (No 1479) that led directly to the creation of the signalbox as we would recognise it today.

Saxby was employed by the LBSCR as a carpenter and joiner, and for some reason took an interest in contemporary signalling. Until his patent, points had been worked by individual levers, station signals by handles on the signalpost, auxiliary or distant signals by levers near to the station signals and connected to the former by wires. In the case of junction signals they were often operated by Stevens & Sons stirrup frames. All these devices were almost always placed in the

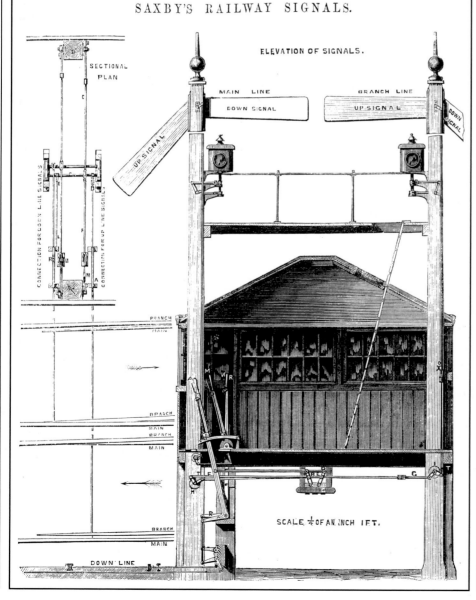

Left (11):
An engraving which appeared in *The Engineer* on 24 September 1858 of John Saxby's 'simultaneous motion' frame.
Author's Collection

open. At stations they were invariably at ground level but at junctions it was more usual to find them on elevated platforms with the semaphores and perhaps the signalman's hut. (A number of these elevated platforms or 'towers' had been built as part of the LNWR's 'Two Mile Telegraph' system in 1855.)

During the 1850s the Board of Trade had tried to persuade companies to bring point and signal controls together, concentrating the mechanisms in a few places around a station or yard layout, the aim being to try and prevent conflicting signals being displayed. Until Saxby's 'simultaneous motion' mechanism, there was no means of doing this; in fact, the story goes that Saxby's inspiration for his invention came from seeing an SER train taking the wrong route at Bricklayers Arms Junction, even though the signalman there had lowered his semaphore to indicate that the points were set for the correct line. With Saxby's equipment, the point blades were connected directly with the appropriate junction signal, so that the wrong indication could never be given, because the moving of the former caused the signal to indicate 'clear' simultaneously. As it was normal practice to keep signals at junctions at danger until a train required to pass over the points, two special levers were built onto the mechanism to enable the main line semaphores to be placed at danger irrespective of the way the points were set, and set-screws could be used on the branch line signals to hold them at danger as well (Picture 11).

The Board of Trade immediately championed the 'simultaneous motion' frame and Saxby felt confident enough to set up his own works at Haywards Heath, leased from his employers the LBSCR. The first place to receive the new mechanism was Keymer Junction (LBSCR), where it was installed on the existing signalling platform in the summer of 1856. Of more significance, however, was its use at Lewes Junction, also on the LBSCR, the following year, where the equipment was fitted into a new, fully glazed timber cabin elevated about 20ft above ground level, with the semaphores protruding through the roof. In evolutionary terms the elevated platform had developed sides and a roof, and become the signalbox.

Lamps and Semaphores

In 1854, William Vitruvius Greenwood and John Saxby secured patents (Nos 683 and 1830) for an arrangement whereby one lamp could be used for showing two different indications simultaneously for trains approaching from two directions. Photographs of these lamps and their operating rods give no indication as to how cleverly constructed they were. Inside the lamp cases were two sets of frames with coloured glasses, so that instead of the whole lamp turning to change aspects, only the glasses inside were moved. The rod for moving one set of glasses passed through the centre of the hollow rod for operating the other set. The handles at the base of the signal post worked in a horizontal

plane on top of each other in the same casting. To operate them the handles were lifted slightly, moved to one of three positions, and held there by one of three studs. Despite this sophistication, originally the movement of the glasses was not connected to the movement of the semaphore arms. The mechanism for this first appeared in Saxby's patent 'simultaneous motion' frame two years later. In this form, the lamps remained popular into the 1870s, and were still in use on the LBSCR in the 1890s.

What became the most common method of changing signal aspects, however, was to use a movable 'spectacle' containing the coloured glasses mounted in front of the lamp lens (Picture 12). It is not known exactly when this arrangement was first used. At first spectacles were completely separate from the semaphores, but eventually from the late 1870s onwards, railway companies began to attach them to the end of the semaphore arm. The weight of the metal frame on one side of the pivot counteracted the weight of the arm on the other, so that if a wire or rod broke the arm would always return to the danger position — 'fail-safe'.

1860-70
A New Generation

By the end of the 1850s, the influence of the generation of railwaymen who had built and operated the first main lines in the 1830s and 1840s was declining. In 1852 Daniel Gooch and Isambard Kingdom Brunel had been able to race an engine along the GWR's main line, relying on their own eyesight and skill to avoid an accident. By the time Brunel died at the age of 53 in 1859, stunts like that were no longer possible. In that year, W. R. Sykes was 19, W. H. Preece was 25, C. E. Spagnoletti was 27, Edward Tyer was 29, John Saxby was 38 and his future partner J. S. Farmer was 32. All these men were the pioneers of a more scientific and less empirical approach to operating railways. During the 1860s, most of the basic equipment that was to revolutionise train control in the 1870s was patented, tried and tested by these men, and between them they laid the foundations of train control that was to survive for over 100 years.

Genesis of the Lever Frame

In December 1859, the NLR's engineer Austen Chambers had installed a hybrid stirrup and lever frame at Kentish Town Junction. The principle was very simple; no signal could be lowered to the clear position until the relevant points had been correctly set for the route signalled, and no other semaphore that might signal a conflicting route could be moved while the levers for the first route were reversed. Unlike Saxby's 'simultaneous motion', the idea behind Chambers' mechanism was 'successive motion'. The potential of this refinement of

Above (12):
A three-position semaphore with spectacle, on the FR at Greenodd. In this position the red glass is in line with the lamp lens. When the arm was inclined down at 45°, the green caution indication (with the yellowish light shining through the blue spectacle glass) was displayed. When the arm was in the all clear position inside the post's slot, the spectacle was pushed clear of the lamp, allowing a 'white' light to be displayed. W. S. Garth

Saxby's mechanism was immediately realised by both John Stevens and Saxby himself, and within a matter of months, both engineers had drawn up designs for a row of levers fully interlocked with each other.

Chambers patented his design and another with just levers in 1860 (Picture 13) but although the principle was progressive, the actual mechanism was not quite up to the job, and it was Stevens and Saxby who exploited the potential of a more sophisticated and reliable lever frame. Stevens installed the first

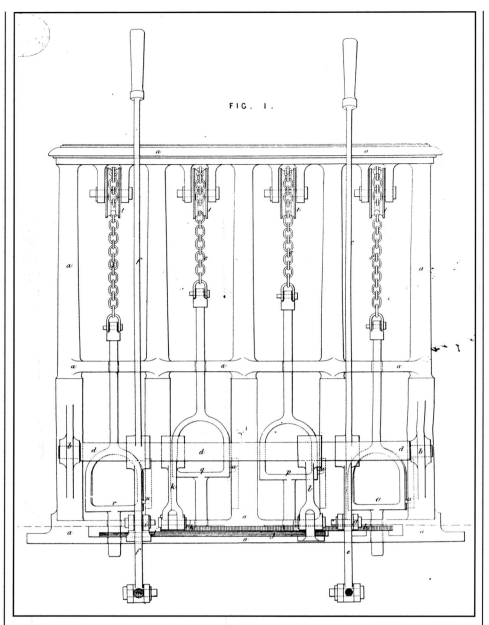

FIG. I.

Left (13):
Engraving from Chambers' patent spec-
ification of 1860 (No 31).
*Reproduced by permission of Birmingham
Library Service*

complimentary for Saxby to use them in subsequent company advertisements, an image of the signalbox becoming his new company trade mark *(Picture 16)*.

In May 1863, Saxby entered into partnership with John Farmer, formerly Assistant Traffic Manager of the LBSCR, and they leased land next to the LNWR at Kilburn to establish their new Patent Railway Signal Works. The choice of the LNWR site was not a coincidence. The company, aware of Saxby's work, had asked him to consider how best to control its Birmingham station, and when he demonstrated that it could be controlled by just two signalmen using his 1860 Patent frames, instead of between 10 and 12 men needed to operate point and signal levers spread all over the layout, the railway company signed a contract with him in 1862 to supply all its signalling needs.

For the next few years, Saxby & Farmer was *the* major force in the signalling market. In 1864, it installed the most complex signalling scheme to date, controlled from seven new signalboxes at and on the approaches to an enlarged London Bridge station and the new terminus at Charing Cross, London. On the LBSCR side of London Bridge, three new signalboxes were erected — South, East and West — with a total of 72 levers. At Charing Cross, opened on 11 January 1864, the new signalbox had actually been considered as part of the architectural detail of the Thames river bridge, the stone abutments designed to support the new structure which straddled the tracks *(Picture 17)*.

All this work in London was helping the Board of Trade to persuade railway companies to install interlocking, and judging from the number of patents for new lever frames in the mid-1860s, the case for interlocking was being won. The first new firm to compete with Stevens & Sons and Saxby & Farmer was McKenzie, Clunes & Holland of Worcester established in 1861, and securing its first patent in 1866 (No 1963). It was this firm which the NLR employed to build and equip four signalboxes for its new terminus at Broad Street, opened at the end of October 1865.

The following year Saxby & Farmer equipped the overhead signalbox at the new Cannon Street station. Measuring 50ft long by only 6ft wide, it was fitted with a 67-lever frame, the largest to date *(Picture 18)*. Thirty-two levers controlled points and another 35 the semaphores. The point levers were painted black, while the up signal levers were painted red, the down ones blue and the distant signal levers were yellow. During the day, two signalmen and two 'lads' were employed on 8hr shifts, the lads working the electric telegraph instruments and calling out what trains were approaching, so that the signalmen could set up the routes. At night one signalman and one lad were employed.

fully interlocked lever frame ahead of Chambers and Saxby, at Yeovil Junction in the spring of 1860, but did not patent his design. Saxby on the other hand made sure his 'invention' was protected (Patent 1860 No 1754) before going into production, accusing Stevens of infringing his patent before he had actually manufactured anything. Saxby lost the case, but it soon became obvious that there were the beginnings of a market for the interlocking lever frame, a growing demand which could support more than one manufacturer.

Two things helped to create that market: firstly a practical demonstration of what was possible, and secondly the realisation that installing interlocking frames and concentrating control at a few places at junctions, stations and yards could actually reduce labour costs, because less signalmen and pointsmen were needed. Both these elements were clearly in evidence at Victoria station, London, which opened in October 1860 and where the very first Saxby interlocking frame was installed. The 23-lever frame was fitted into a room open at the front,

and because it was the first interlocking frame to be photographed, this 'Hole-in-the-Wall' signalbox became an influential image at the time and one which Saxby ensured was used for publicity purposes, then and for years to come *(Picture 14)*.

Its location and design were, however, very unusual, and from then on, lever frames were usually installed in fully glazed signalboxes. In 1861, while Saxby was still working for the LBSCR, a number of his new frames were fitted along that company's Shoreham to Horsham line, and the following year he was asked by his employers to provide the new signalling equipment at Brighton station *(Picture 15)*, a contract that persuaded him he could leave the railway and rely totally on his signalling contracts. All this was good publicity for Saxby, and when his design of signalbox at Stewarts Lane Junction, Battersea (LBSCR), with its 23 levers and 10 semaphore arms fitted to the two posts emerging from the roof, was inspected by Captain Tyler of the Railway Inspectorate of the Board of Trade on 11 August 1862, his remarks were sufficiently

It was at Cannon Street that the principle and importance of interlocking was really confirmed. It took some time for the signalmen to become familiar with the interlocking on the opening day, 1 September 1866, and because trains were being delayed, the SER's general manager considered removing the locking. Fortunately, before this could be done, the signalmen had mastered the frame and proved that interlocking could be both safe and cope with an intense service over a complex layout.

The Cannon Street work was followed in 1866/7 by the re-equipping of Victoria station with five new signalboxes to replace the Hole-in-the-Wall, while at the same time, Stevens & Sons was busy installing the signalling at the LSWR's Waterloo terminus.

Above (14):
A photograph of the 'Hole-in-the-Wall' signalbox at Victoria station, which appeared in Saxby & Farmer's trade catalogue of 1901.
Transport Trust Library

Right (15):
The spartan interior of Saxby's Brighton North signalbox, built in 1862 and equipped with 37 levers manufactured to the 1860 Patent (No 1754). The different travel of the levers is very obvious. The 'travel' was the distance the lever had to be pulled by the signalman from its normal (almost upright) position in the frame to its fully reversed position (sloping towards the signalman). The 11 levers in the middle of the frame, with very short travels, operated the semaphores, while the levers either side operated the points. This photograph also comes from Saxby & Farmer's 1901 trade catalogue.
Transport Trust Library

The main signalbox there, which like those at Charing Cross, Cannon Street and London Bridge straddled the track, was brought into use in March 1867. It was fitted with two frames arranged in parallel, containing 24 levers for main line trains and 23 levers for signals and points on the Windsor side of the station. Eight additional signals were controlled from a stirrup frame.

Competition

By then, both Saxby & Farmer and Stevens & Sons were realising that the locking in their 1860-type frames was wearing badly, compromising the integrity of the interlocking. It appears that everyone at Saxby's Kilburn works was searching for a solution and in the spring of 1867 Walter Easterbrook, an employee, applied for a patent for 'catch handle locking'. Instead of the movement of the whole lever activating the locks, the action of the catch handles of the levers was used instead. Until then, the catch handle had simply raised or lowered a block which held the lever in either its normal or reversed position in the frame. In the new design, the rod connecting the catch handle to the block was extended through the latter into the locking below, so that instead of the locking being subjected to the full force of a signalman pulling at a lever, only the pressure of grasping the catch handle was transmitted to the locks. When Saxby found out about Easterbrook's patent application, he promptly lodged one of his own and then dismissed his employee.

Easterbrook's application was successful (No 927) but so too was Saxby's (1867 No 2119), partly due to the fact that he had had time to study his new rival's drawings (*Picture 19*). Saxby soon began to manufacture new frames with catch handle locking and Easterbrook took out two further patents — Nos 2143 of July 1867 and 509 of 1868 — going into production with the latter after winning his first contract that year.

Stevens & Sons' solution for improving its interlocking proved to be a milestone in frame

Top left (16):
Saxby's signalbox at Stewarts' Lane, photographed in December 1886. The lamps are examples made to Saxby & Greenwood's Patent of 1854 (Nos 683 and 1830). The coloured glasses for both directions were inside the lamp case, which contained a single flame to shine a light through two lenses set at 180° to each other.
Ian Allan, Madgwick Collection

Centre left (17):
The overhead signalbox at Charing Cross, photographed shortly after it opened in 1864. The point rodding was neatly taken down to track level inside the piers supporting the signalbox and once at that level the rods were boxed in. *Ian Allan, Bucknall Collection*

Left (18):
The interior of the 1866 overhead signalbox controlling Cannon Street station another photograph which appeared in Saxby & Farmer's 1901 catalogue.
Transport Trust Library

design, although the firm could have had no idea at the time it was patented (1870, No 746). The actual mechanism was devised by James Deakin, an employee of Stevens, but patented in the name of the company. It was subsequently known as tappet locking. The first experimental frame incorporating both tappet and Stevens' original 1860 'hook' interlocking was installed at Hardengreen Junction on the NBR in June 1868. This was followed in the same year by two other installations in Scotland, the 72-lever frame fitted at Kilmarnock for the GSWR having just tappet locking. Stevens frames with this form of interlocking remained in production for almost 100 years, during which time they were supplied to almost every railway company in the country. Inexplicably, the firm failed to pay the next instalment on the patent in 1873, and when other firms began to appreciate the flexibility this type of locking offered, as the demands on locking became more complex in the 1880s, almost all other signalling manufacturer's and railway companies' own designs of frame were adapted to make use of it.

By the end of the 1860s, competition in the mechanical signalling market was increasing, with the emergence in 1867 of E. I'Anson & Sons & Co of Darlington and E. S. Yardley & Co of Manchester, followed by Ransomes & Rapier of Ipswich, which started to make its own lever frame in 1869.

Development of the Block Instrument

It is all too easy to believe that progress is cumulative, that given time, things inevitably improve. But progress is not one smooth upward curve, and the story of the block system in the 1860s illustrates this point very well.

As mentioned before, various railway companies began to use the block system in the 1850s on sections of their double track main lines. Unfortunately, as traffic increased at the end of that decade, both the LNWR and the GNR abandoned the absolute block system and began to modify its operation so as to allow more than one train in a section at any one time. This became known later as the 'permissive block system'. The compromise was a great disappointment to the Board of Trade which had been trying for years to persuade companies to adopt absolute block working.

Apart from through the tunnels, the GNR relaxed its block regulations at various places between King's Cross and Hitchin in 1860. If a section was already occupied by a train, the following one was cautioned by the signalman and the driver instructed to proceed at no more than 15mph until he arrived at the next signal station. The LNWR used a similar but, it was claimed, safer system.

This trend towards permissive block working did not last long, however, because a number of accidents showed how dangerous such a system could be. The accident in Clayton Tunnel on the LBSCR in 1861 persuaded that company to establish the

absolute block system along its Brighton main line, and it appears that this was completed in the first months of 1863, using twin-needle instruments designed by a Mr Bartholomew. Another two accidents involving one train running into the rear of another on the GNR, one just outside Rossington in June and the other at Colney Hatch in August 1865, persuaded that company to reintroduce absolute block working. (As a result of the Colney Hatch accident, the company had had to settle 250 compensation claims.) The Bristol & Exeter Railway started to introduce absolute block working in 1861 and by 1867 all its lines were so protected. Further pressure was put on companies in 1869, following a survey by the Board of Trade into methods of train control, and when it seemed that the Board might impose block working at the beginning of the 1870s, companies all over the country began to abandon the time interval system.

What also helped with the introduction of the absolute block system was the availability of a number of specially designed block instruments. During the 1850s, the LNWR, GNR and GER used electric telegraph instruments with single needles to indicate whether the line was clear or not. On the L&YR, Highton's disc instruments were used, and on the SER, C. V. Walker's miniature semaphore instruments were becoming available. The three new instruments developed in the 1860s each adopted one of these three indication methods: needle, disc, or semaphore.

Edward Tyer

The most successful was Tyer's one-wire, two-position block instrument. Edward Tyer had taken out his first patent for what was in effect automatic signalling at the start of 1852, but it was ahead of its time and the electrical equipment needed to operate it successfully was not yet reliable, so it was not

adopted. During the next 10 years he continued to develop and patent other unique devices for train signalling, and eventually it was his simple-to-install and cost-effective block instruments which could be straightforwardly manipulated by signalmen that established his company as the most important manufacturer of electrical signalling equipment in the world.

In 1862, he was granted a patent (No 3015) for a block instrument obviously based on Clark's work, but with all the four needles required for controlling a double line either side of a signal station incorporated into one case. Instead of handles to operate the needles, the instrument had brass plungers. Some railway managers probably felt it was too confusing for ordinary signalman to understand but there were two powerful selling points which when incorporated into later Tyer's instruments finally convinced many to purchase:

1) Only one wire was needed to connect instruments at either end of a block section (with the usual earth return) compared with the three wires needed to operate Clark's block instruments. Tyer's single-wire, earth return circuit, included a single-stroke bell and/or gong, whereas Clark's bells and needles all required separate circuits.

2) There was a considerable saving on battery power because the instruments did not use continuous currents to maintain the needles at either line clear or train on line, as did instruments used by the LNWR. By pressing down one of the appropriate plungers

on the front of the instrument case, the circuit was activated between the 'sending' and 'receiving' instruments. The appropriate plunger rang either the bell or gong, and while it was depressed, the current temporarily magnetised metal pieces around the appropriate needles on both the sending and receiving instruments. When the plunger was released, thereby stopping the flow of current, the metal pieces retained their magnetism, thus maintaining the needles at one of two possible indications — line clear or train on line.

Over the next few years, Tyer refined the electrical mechanisms of his instrument, particularly in the area of counteracting the effects of lightning, and when Patent No 2907 was granted to him in 1869, he had all the elements to enable him to create what became one of the most commercially successful block instruments. Instead of putting all the needles into one case, he adopted Clark's idea of producing an instrument with two needles, so that two identical instruments would be needed for each signalbox controlling ordinary double track. A separate plunger was provided with each set, so that the bell or gong could be activated without the signalman inadvertently changing the indication of the needles, and in this form, as also in a version with miniature semaphore arms substituted for the needles, Tyer's Train Signalling Telegraph instruments became popular with a number of important railway companies in the 1870s *(Picture 20)*.

It was not just Tyer's instruments that gained acceptance on many railways, but his procedures for the sending and receiving of messages on the bells and gongs used with his instruments, as well as the bell codes themselves, which laid the foundations for later (and modern) block working. For example, Tyer advocated one beat of the bell or gong to call the attention of a signalman; on the LNWR and other railways, the needle was moved from side to side to attract the attention of the adjacent signalman. In Tyer's code, four beats of the bell signified an express train; this code remains the same today.

Charles E. Spagnoletti

The second most influential and long-lived block instrument patented during the 1860s was Spagnoletti's three-wire, two-position block instrument. Spagnoletti had worked for the Electric Telegraph Co before moving to the GWR in 1855 and, therefore, he would also have been aware of Edwin Clark's work on the LNWR. Not surprisingly, when he developed a block instrument for the GWR he too based his ideas around the principle of the single needle. The patent for his device was granted at the beginning of 1863, No 2297 *(Picture 21)*, but instead of a vertical needle pointing to a description, as in Clark's instrument, Spagnoletti attached to the top of his needle a card (referred to in the patent as a 'screen' and later in more common usage as a 'disc') on which were printed opposite each other the words 'line clear' on a white ground, and 'train on line' on a red ground. In his block instrument the needle was then mounted behind a painted metal screen, in which there was a small rectangular aperture through which one of the printed indications would show when the current was flowing in the appropriate direction.

To complete the circuit so that 'line clear' showed in the aperture, the left-hand one of two 'tappers' (or 'finger keys' as stated in the patent) protruding from the front of the instrument was held down by a metal peg. When that was released, the peg was then used to hold down the right-hand finger key, causing 'train on line' to be displayed in the aperture. The 'line clear' tapper had a white end, while the 'train on line' one had a red end. As with Clark's and Tyer's instruments, the normal indication was 'line clear', only changed by the signalman to 'train on line' when a train entered the block section.

The Metropolitan Railway, from its opening in January 1863, used the block system, regulated with Spagnoletti's instruments, and this company also adopted

Above (20):
Three Tyer's one-wire, two-position semaphore block instruments still in use at the former LBSCR Birchden Junction signalbox in March 1985. *Kim Fullbrook*

Below (21):
Front and side elevations of Spagnoletti's block instrument, engraved for the patent specification of 1863 (No 2297). *Reproduced by permission of Birmingham Library Service*

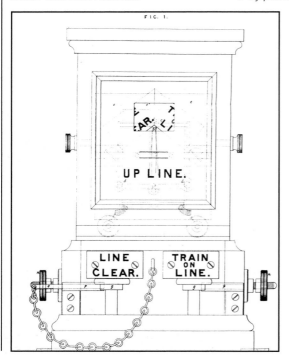

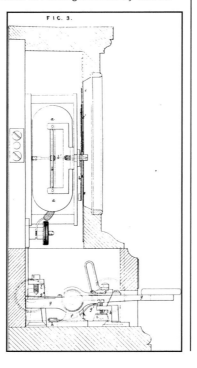

his 'lock and block' version when that was developed a few years later. With the refinement of the block system in the 1870s, the pegging instrument was joined by a 'non-pegging' variation, a needle unit in an identical case but without the finger keys. If a train was going forward into a block section, the signalman in advance (ie the far end of the block section) pegged down 'train on line' as before, but the indication was repeated at the end the train was being sent from, on the non-pegging instrument. As three separate instruments were required to control the passage of trains between adjacent signalboxes — a pegger (for one line), non-pegger (for the other line) and single-stroke bell — and each of those instruments was connected by its own wire (with earth return), the terminology to describe Spagnoletti's (and others') continuous current system was 'three-wire'.

Of all the early block instruments, Spagnoletti's changed the least after it had been patented. The only significant modifications in later instruments were the attaching of the descriptions to the bottom of the needle instead of the top, the replacement of the peg and chain by a loop of wire, and, much later, the combining of the pegging and non-pegging indications in one case and the addition of brass reminder flaps which could be dropped down over the finger keys to prevent the signalman from depressing them.

William H. Preece

The final new block instrument of the 1860s was Preece's three-wire, two-position block instrument. W. H. Preece, who became the LSWR's Superintendent of Telegraphs in 1860, had worked as Edwin Clark's assistant while at the Electric Telegraph Co and therefore was completely familiar with the LNWR's block system. The LSWR's telegraph office at Southampton used both single- and double-needle telegraph instruments to transmit messages, but when

Preece came to devise instruments for controlling the block system (1862, patent No 77) he decided they should not inform the signalman as to the state of the line, but should be concerned with the fixed signals and their indications, just as C. V. Walker's experimental instrument of 1854. (It is interesting to note that Preece was unaware of Walker's instrument when he patented his own version in 1862.)

To this end, Preece created three physically separate, but electrically linked, devices. The most striking was a wooden case from which protruded a tall metal post, at the top of which was a single miniature semaphore arm. The second device was another rectangular case in which a needle indicated whether the signal was 'off' or 'on', and the third was a miniature lever, described by Preece as a 'switch key'.

Signalmen communicated by single-stroke bells, and the fundamental idea was that once a train had been allowed to enter a clear block section, the signalman who was to receive the train, operated the miniature lever which raised to danger the miniature semaphore arm at the end from which the train was approaching. This prompted the signalman there to place his fixed signal to danger, thus preventing another train from entering the section. While the miniature semaphore arm was in the danger position, the needle pointed to the word 'on' on the other instrument at the far end of the section, to confirm to the signalman there who was awaiting the train that the miniature semaphore at the 'departure' end was displaying the correct indication.

Once the train had arrived safely, the signalman put his miniature lever to the 'off' position (which would be indicated by the word 'off' in the other instrument) and the miniature semaphore at the end from which the train had come would disappear into its metal post — the accepted all clear position — telling the signalman there that he could once again lower his outdoor semaphore.

The first installation of Preece's equipment on the LSWR was between Queen Street and St David's stations, Exeter, in March 1862. One of the first companies other than the LSWR to install Preece's instruments was the Glasgow & Paisley Joint Railway. Signal stations were established every two miles on its Wemyss Bay Branch, and by July 1865 it was the company's intention to extend the block system to all its lines.

In 1865 Preece patented a version of his miniature lever (No 2016) which he intended to be used in conjunction with a wheel-operated treadle. Once put to danger, the lever was locked in that position until the train passed over the treadle, which freed it for another 'line clear' pull. Later the on/off indicator gained a circular face, behind which the single-stroke bell was mounted.

The following year, Preece produced a one-wire (momentary current) version of his semaphore instrument, and in 1872 the miniature semaphore, bell and on/off indications were incorporated into a single wooden case. By then, all clear was indicated when the miniature semaphore was inclined at 45°. Eventually the three-wire version — ie the original 1862 patent — was treated in the same way, with its own wooden case for all the component parts except the miniature lever (Picture 22).

Below left (22):
An example of Preece's three-wire, two-position block instrument, after the component parts had been combined into one wooden case very similar to the 1872 one-wire version. (NB: the 'on'/'off' indication has been removed.) *Author's Collection*

Below (23):
Severn Bridge Junction, Shrewsbury, in the early 1870s, showing the first fully interlocked signalbox at this location. The semaphores above the box have perforated arms, indicating that the signalling was probably installed by Stevens & Sons.
Shropshire Library & Record Service

1870-89

The Revolution

The railways of the 1860s would still have been a strange organisation to our eyes despite certain 'modern' features (*Picture 23*). But railway managers of the 1990s would recognise the operation of Britain's railways in the 1870s. In that decade, no new lines were opened without signals, signalboxes, interlocking frames and block instruments, and gradually existing lines were re-equipped too. There were still a few dissenting voices, claiming that the block system had been forced on railway managers and that it increased expenditure. But in reality the arguments of the 1860s had been won. With the number and speed of trains increasing, the block system was the only way of safely handling traffic (*Picture 24*).

Signalboxes

In this period standardisation became more noticeable. For example, although every railway company and a number of contractors developed their own styles of signalboxes, all shared so many basic characteristics that signalboxes were instantly recognisable as such, no matter were they were built, all over the country.

By 1874, the GNR had erected just over 100 new ones on its 162 miles of main line between King's Cross and Askern (just north of Doncaster), replacing its first generation of elevated platforms, towers and huts (*Picture 25*). They were all constructed to the company's first standard design, the main elements of which were continued in all subsequent designs right into the 20th century.

On the other side of the country, the LNWR had 88 signalboxes in use by 1874, controlling the 132 miles between Euston and Stafford. The majority of those were also new structures, built to the LNWR's first standard design. By 1874, of the company's total of 1,119 miles of double track, over half was already protected by the absolute block system. The same rash of building and installation of block working happened on most of the country's main lines in this period, the GNR and LNWR being only two examples used here to illustrate a larger trend (*Picture 26*).

Signalmen

It was during the 1870s that the status of the signalman began to improve. They were still not as highly paid as engine drivers, but they were given bonuses for good conduct and had the opportunity of promotion as signalboxes themselves began to be classified. On the Metropolitan Railway they were well trained and highly regarded, Richard Rapier remarking in his paper to the Institution of Civil Engineers in 1874 that one third were ex-sailors, 'It (being) found that sailors make excellent signalmen, but soldiers do not.' No explanation was given for this comment.

On the LNWR, new signalmen were given at least two weeks' training at the signalbox they were to man, and in addition had to have a certificate from the District Superintendent, confirming that they could read, write, judge distances, distinguish colours, understand telegraphy and the company's rules. At what

Below (24):
This photograph by T. Annan of Glasgow, of St Nicholas Crossing, Carlisle, taken in 1876 just before the flat crossing and associated signalling was abolished, gives a good impression of the mixed standard of 1860s equipment. The semaphores tell drivers when but not where to stop their trains. Even then it is far from clear what all the arms refer to, especially the gas-lit one in the foreground which might be an auxiliary or a stop signal.
Cumbria Heritage Services (Carlisle Library)

Right (25):
LNER 'A4' *Silver King* passes Egmanton signalbox midway between Retford and Newark in 1947. The GNR opened this box in November 1871 and it remained in continual use until 24 October 1976. In the bottom left of the photograph is the signalling hut of the 1860s it replaced.
J. F. Henton/National Railway Museum

Below right (26):
An example of the MR's first standard signalbox and semaphore signal, photographed at Mansfield Woodhouse shortly after the opening of the Mansfield-Worksop line on 1 June 1875.
Pegg Collection, Mansfield Library

were considered important signalboxes, men worked 8hr shifts, at lesser boxes 10hr and at others 12hr shifts, which meant only two signalmen were needed.

By the end of the period under consideration, the status of signalmen had improved and many were held in the same regard as engine drivers. But 12hr shifts were still common, and the fear of dismissal was still a management tool to enforce loyalty and discipline.

Semaphores

During the 1870s all railway companies, including the GWR, began to standardise on semaphore signals, gradually abandoning boards, disc and crossbars, etc. At first the double arm station signal continued as the standard 'station semaphore' but its main disadvantage was that it only told a driver when to stop or proceed, not where to stop. A driver had to know exactly where to halt his train without obstructing points and/or fouling other train movements. So gradually single arm semaphores were positioned as close as possible to where a driver was expected to pull up and, apart from at terminal stations, the practice of positioning semaphores above signalboxes was abandoned.

The station semaphore became the 'home' signal and it was usually supplemented by another semaphore a few hundred yards in advance of it — the 'starting' or 'starter' signal. As a driver had to stop if either of these signals was in the danger position ('on'), both were designated 'stop' signals. In areas where traffic was heavy, it was operationally better to have a number of closely spaced stop signals to keep the trains moving signal to signal, and gradually through the 1880s the home and starting semaphores were joined by other stop signals, known by different names on different lines, but often referred to as 'inner home', 'outer home' and 'advanced starter'.

Often 1,000yd in rear of the stop signals was the distant signal. As mentioned in the last chapter, the distant or auxiliary signal had developed in the late 1840s as a means of giving a driver prior warning of the indication of the main station semaphore, giving him time to start braking his train. During the 1860s the distant could be lowered even if the station signal was on, allowing the driver to be

signalled passed it. By the end of the decade, judging from the reports of various accidents, it was becoming the usual practice for drivers not to stop at distants in the on position. This anticipated the way in which distant signals were treated when the block system was fully developed in the following decade, because whether the distant was on or off, no train could enter a block section unless the line was clear to the main — home — signal.

In the 1870s, the distant signal became the means of informing a driver whether or not all the stop signals he was approaching were in the clear (off) or danger (on) position. In Stevens & Sons' 1870 tappet frames the locking was so arranged that the distant signal could not be lowered until all the stop signals were in the off position, and this principle was incorporated into subsequent interlocking frames, although there were exceptions. Drivers could, of course, pass the distant whether it indicated on or off, but the advance warning it gave of the state of the signals ahead was considered so important that in fog or falling snow, platelayers (or other available staff) were drafted in as fogmen, to ensure that detonators were placed on the line whenever the distant was in the on position to give drivers an audible indication of its aspect. One of the very last places in the country

where distants could be lowered completely independently of the indication of home and starting signals was on the GNSR, where the Board of Trade condemned the practice as late as 1898.

By the 1890s, there were as many different designs of semaphore arms (and fittings) as there were railway companies and signalling contractors but, nevertheless, all were made to display their indications on the left-hand side of the posts they were mounted on, whether wooden or metal lattice construction. All indicated danger when horizontal and at 90° to the post, and all clear when inclined downwards from that horizontal position, this indication being made in the 'lower quadrant' *(Picture 27)*.

Lever Frames

After 1870, most railway companies established Signal and Telegraph Departments to maintain all this new equipment, and a number started to manufacture and repair their own, both electrical and mechanical. The GNR, MSLR, NER, MR, CLC, LNWR, NLR, L&YR, GWR, LBSCR, SER and the Metropolitan all made their own interlocking frames at some time, but only the MR,

LNWR, GWR and L&YR produced their own designs in any quantity. The majority of these companies also used contractors' lever frames as well as their own, with the notable exception of the MR, which from 1869 until 1921 used only frames made at its works in Derby. In common with other railways, the MR never patented its distinctive design, the only company to do so being the LNWR, which became self-sufficient in all mechanical signalling hardware after 1874 *(Picture 28)*.

As the demand grew for interlocking frames and other mechanical signalling equipment, Saxby & Farmer, Stevens & Sons, McKenzie & Holland, Courtney & Stephens, Easterbrook & Co, E. I'Anson & Sons & Co, E. S. Yardley & Co and Ransomes & Rapier mentioned above, were joined in the signalling market by a number of new firms:

William Baines & Co, Smethwick	1870s
Crumlin Viaduct Co, Crumlin	1871
J. Tweedy & Co, Carlisle	1873
Gloucester Wagon Co, Gloucester	(1860)
(began making signalling equipment in 1876)	
The Railway Signal Co, Fazakerley	1881
Dutton & Co, Worcester	1888
Evans, O'Donnell, Chippenham	1894
J. F. Pease & Co Ltd, Middlesbrough	1899
(taking over assets of Dutton & Co)	

The competition for contracts was intense and not all firms survived. Costs were driven down, encouraging the older companies to redesign their equipment, and between 1870 and 1889, 64 different designs of interlocking lever frames were patented, compared to 36 between 1856 and 1869 (inclusive) and 20 between 1890 and 1897. Some were never produced in any quantity, others wore out quickly or proved incapable of modification. But many outlasted the firms which made and fitted them, and a number are still in active service at the time of writing (1997). The most successful and widely used contractors designs made after 1870 are listed below.

Of the new firms and their designs, the Railway Signal Co was the only one that rivalled Stevens & Sons, Saxby & Farmer and McKenzie & Holland in any significant way,

the latter companies dominating the market until World War 1. Saxby continued to take his rivals to court, apparently resenting any competition. McKenzie & Holland survived a protracted battle at the beginning of the 1870s, as did the Gloucester Wagon Co between 1879 and 1883. Easterbrook's attempt to turn the tables and sue his former employer between 1883 and 1885, however, proved fatal for his business.

Saxby did not pursue Stevens & Sons again after losing his 1860 case, but he obviously never forgot the encounter. It must have been with some satisfaction that his firm won the contract to replace the original 1867 signalbox with its pair of Stevens 1860-type frames at the LSWR's London terminus at Waterloo. In 1874 a new overhead signalbox was erected, with one of Saxby & Farmer's 1871 Patent Rocker frames containing 108 levers. The triumph was short-lived, however, because only four years later the Saxby signalbox was 'encased' (as a 1905 *Railway Magazine* article described the event) and 35 extra levers were added by Stevens & Sons. A further 20 levers were installed in 1880, and 65 more added five years later, bringing the

total to 228. Then in 1892 a completely new signalbox was built and equipped with two brand-new Stevens frames. Even though old rivalries must have cooled by then, and Saxby & Farmer no longer manufactured examples of its 1871 Patent Rocker frames, the company still felt it relevant to illustrate the 1874 Waterloo frame in its 1901 trade catalogue, commenting rather bitterly that, 'this apparatus has since been swept away'.

Other Mechanical Developments

This period was not all signalboxes and locking frames, however. Out on the track a number of mechanisms were brought into use

Firm	Design	Patent number or first year of manufacture
Stevens & Sons	Stevens Glasgow Old Pattern	1870 No 746
	Stevens Glasgow New Pattern	(not patented) 1890s
	Stevens/Caledonian	(not patented) *c*1897
Saxby & Farmer	Saxby & Farmer 1871 Patent Rocker	1871 No 1601
	Saxby & Farmer 1874 Rocker & Gridiron	1874 No 294
	Saxby & Farmer 1888 Duplex	1888 No 183
McKenzie & Holland	McKenzie & Holland 1873 Patent	1873 No 2034
	McKenzie & Holland 1886 Patent (Nos 9/11/12)	1886 No 4355
	McKenzie & Holland Cam & Tappet (Nos 13/14)	(not patented) *c*1893
	McKenzie & Holland Nos 16/17	(not patented) 1903
Easterbrook	Easterbrook 1872 Patent	1872 No 1606
Gloucester Wagon Co	Gloucester Wagon Co	1877 No 947
Railway Signal Co	Railway Signal Co 1877 Patent	1877 No 947[1] *(Picture 29)*
	Railway Signal Co Tappet	(not patented) 1884
Dutton & Co	Dutton 1893 Patent	1893 No 1343
Evans, O'Donnell & Co	Evans, O'Donnell	(based on) 1891 No 1463

[1]This patent was in the name of George Edwards who left the Gloucester Wagon Co to establish his own firm — the Railway Signal Co — in 1881.

(NB except in a few cases, most of the design names are not those used by the firms but were allocated to them by the Signalling Study Group in 1989.)

Left (28):
On the operating floor the various LNWR patent frame designs were indistinguishable from each other. The most distinctive feature on all the frames compared with other types was the means of lifting the catch-block which held the lever in its normal or reversed position. On LNWR frames, instead of a catch-handle behind the top of the lever, there was a stirrup handle in front, which was what the signalman's left hand was grasping when this photograph was taken inside Preston No 4 signalbox in 1946. The signalbox was opened in 1900 with a frame of 164 levers.
Ian Allan Library

Below left (29):
Salthouse Junction signalbox, Barrow on the FR photographed just before World War 1. The lever frame is an example of the Railway Signal Co tappet locking design of the 1880s. On the block shelf are two Tyer's one-wire three-position block instruments manufactured to the firm's 1902 patent (No 9284).
The Sankey Collection, No 7523

(and many patented of course) to improve safety. Facing point locks held point blades firmly in position while locking bars prevented signalmen from accidentally moving them as trains passed over. At sidings where one train might collide with another while being shunted, fouling bars were laid to prevent signals being lowered if the vehicles standing on one track were too close to another line. Mechanical 'detectors' were brought into use, in which the signal wire was prevented from operating the signal if the point blades were not correctly set. Gradually more shunting signals, or ground signals, were provided at points to control shunting movements, replacing the need for signalmen to communicate with drivers using hand signals, flags or hand lamps *(Picture 30)*.

Where sidings were beyond the direct mechanical control of signalboxes, separate ground frames were provided to work the points. In 1875, J. E. Annett patented (No 3427) a mechanism which was akin to a door lock to protect such sidings. His lock was attached to the lever in the signalbox which operated the main signals allowing trains onto the stretch of line where the remote siding was located. When the key was removed from this lock, the lever could not be reversed, so that the key could be taken by the train crew to the siding to unlock the ground frame there, protected by the section signals being locked at danger. 'Annett's keys' became very familiar to generations of shunters.

Lock and Block

On the electrical side there were also innovations. Devices for repeating the indications of semaphores out of sight of signalmen became more common. Some instruments incorporated miniature semaphore arms, others had discs or single needles. A number were also able to tell the

signalman whether signal lamps were alight or not. Special instruments were manufactured so that signalmen could keep a tally of the number of trains occupying sections of line controlled by the permissive block system. So that signalmen could inform each other which of a number of routes a train should take, train describers were produced, which listed the possible destinations on circular dials, needles rather like the hands of a clock being used to point to the desired indications *(Picture 31)*.

The most significant of electrical developments, however, was 'lock and block'. One of the criticisms of block working was that it could only be effective and safe if the signalmen operating it were entirely conscientious. There was nothing to prevent a signalman lowering his signal and allowing a train in to a section even if it was already occupied and he had not received a 'line clear' from the signalbox in advance. The idea of 'lock and block' was to ensure that this never happened, that the signal controlling entry into a block section was physically locked until the signalman in advance had confirmed the line was clear and released that signal lock. It also became important that trains had proved that they had passed completely through the section before another could be allowed to follow.

Various experiments had been carried out from as early as the 1840s, with train-

operated semaphores, lever locks, etc but it was not until the block system had been fully developed that engineers had a definite framework in which they could create a workable system.

The person whose name became synonymous with lock and block was William Robert (W. R.) Sykes. In 1874 while employed by the LCDR, he carried out experiments between Shepherds Lane, Brixton and Canterbury Road Junction signalboxes, and his first patent based on this work was obtained the following year, 1875 No 662 *(Picture 32)*.

Single-stroke bells were still used to communicate between signalboxes, and Sykes obviously intended standard block instruments to remain in use as well. The home signal controlling entry into the block section was maintained at danger until required to be cleared to allow a train past, contrary to the accepted practice of the day. The lock and block instrument which was connected by a rod to the home signal lever, consisted of an upright oblong box with two circular openings one above the other.

If three signalboxes, A, B and C, are used as an example, then the normal indication in the lower opening of the instrument at B was a red disc, which covered a fixed white board lettered 'TRAIN FROM A'. The upper opening showed 'CLEAR TO C' on a white disc which covered a fixed board coloured red. This

indication was equivalent to 'line clear', the normal position of all block instruments at this date. With the instrument showing these indications, B's home signal would have been locked. Only when it was 'proved' that a train was approaching from A was the semaphore released, achieved when A pulled his signal off to allow the train forward to B. The red disc in the instrument at B then dropped down to reveal 'TRAIN FROM A' in the lower opening, simultaneously sounding a gong, and releasing the lock on B's home signal.

When B then pulled his home signal lever, both openings in his instrument showed red, at the same time unlocking the lever in the signalbox at C. When B replaced his semaphore to danger behind the train, it became locked again, while the circuitry unlocked the home signal at A. In other words, the signalman at A was physically prevented from reversing his home signal lever to allow another train forward to B, until the signalman there had placed his semaphore to danger behind the first train. The same 'proving' of the train through the section continued when C put his home signal to danger behind the train, unlocking the home signal at B, and so the procedure was repeated.

By the end of the 1870s, Sykes had completely redesigned the equipment and in November 1880 he took out a patent (No 1907) for a new instrument. It consisted

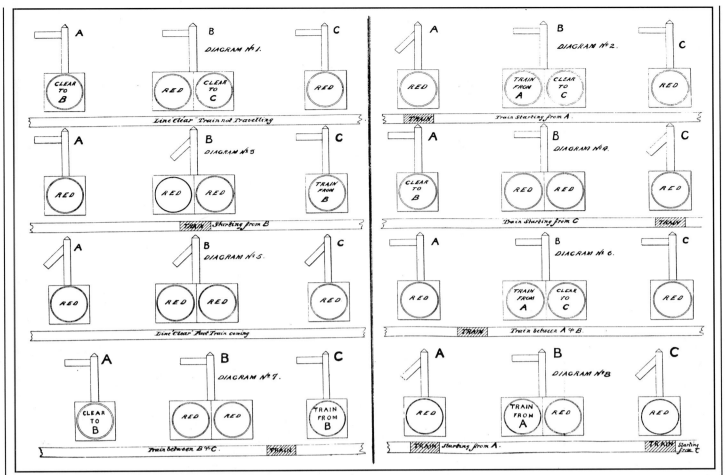

of a rectangular wooden case with a glazed circular face, behind which were two rectangular apertures. In these openings two separate flags or 'tablets' could be displayed, the top one indicating either 'LOCKED' or 'CLEAR' (the terminology later changed to 'FREE'), while the bottom one indicated either 'TRAIN ON', or 'TRAIN PASSED', 'PASSED' or just blank. Above the wooden case, a miniature semaphore arm with a short brass post was mounted in a cylindrical tin case with a glass front.

Unlike the 1875 system, the release for the lever lock at B was given by pressing a plunger on the instrument at C. When this release was given, 'TRAIN ON' was displayed in the lower aperture of C's instrument, while at the same time the miniature semaphore on the instrument at B changed from the clear to the danger position, and 'CLEAR' (or later 'FREE') appeared in B's upper aperture. The signalman at B could then pull off the signal controlling entry into the section. Once the signal was pulled off, the upper aperture displayed 'LOCKED'. A treadle was also introduced into the system, placed just beyond the home or starting signal (depending on which controlled entry in to the block section) which, when the last vehicle of the train had passed clear of it, released the lock on the

lever controlling that signal, changing the upper aperture display from 'LOCKED' to 'CLEAR', allowing the signalman to place the semaphore to danger. Once at danger, the lever was again locked, with 'LOCKED' displayed in the upper aperture. When the train arrived at C and the signalman there replaced his semaphore to danger behind it, the lower aperture in his instrument changed from 'TRAIN ON' to 'TRAIN PASSED', 'CLEAR' or blank, and at the same time lowered the miniature semaphore arm in B's instrument, indicating that the line was once again clear.

Building on the 1880 patent, Sykes soon added a 'switch hook' to the main instrument which was used to turn over the plunger. When the train entered the section and the appropriate bell code was sent to the signalman in advance, that signalman turned this switch hook over the plunger on his instrument. Turning the switch hook raised the miniature semaphore arm to danger at the sending end. Other refinements followed, for example allowing the section signal to be put to danger in cases of emergency before the train had passed over the treadle and released the lock. In these circumstances, the lever was not restored fully to its normal position in the frame, but just far enough to allow the semaphore arm to return to the danger position without releasing the interlocking in the lever frame. At junctions, the circuitry could be so arranged that the points had to be correctly set before a train could be accepted on the plunging instrument, and once that was done, no other train could be accepted on a converging line.

In this form, Sykes Lock and Block was installed on most of the suburban lines south of the River Thames, as well as on the Hull & Barnsley Railway when that opened in July 1885, and the Lancashire, Derbyshire & East Coast Railway when that opened in December 1896. On these lines where home and starting signals were used, two instruments controlled each line. The plunging instrument contained the lock for the home signal, its normal condition being 'FREE' until the arm had been lowered, after which it remained locked until the train had passed it. The other instrument, without the plunger, and referred to by the northern companies as the 'electrical instrument', contained the lock for the starting signal, normally locked until a release (a plunge) had been given by the signalman in advance. This instrument also carried above it the miniature semaphore arm. Both the Hull & Barnsley and the Lancashire, Derbyshire & East Coast operated 'open block' sections, with the miniature semaphore normally lowered to indicate that the section was unoccupied. A version with a three-position needle indication in place of the top semaphore was also used by the NBR.

In 1896 probably the most sophisticated version of Sykes Lock and Block was installed on the GER out of London. Basically the instruments operated as described above, but with an additional indication of 'TRAIN ACCEPTED' as well as 'TRAIN ON'. But that was not the only change. The Achilles' heel of previous Sykes instruments had been the release key. This could be used in two ways: (1) to raise the 'TRAIN ON' indication and thus

Companies that used Sykes Lock and Block	
LBSCR	Suburban lines. ('Open block', ie top semaphore's normal position lowered — 'clear'.)
SER	Suburban lines. ('Open block')
LCDR	Plunger instrument used in conjunction with Sykes double semaphore instrument. In the London area, telegraph instruments were used instead of block bells. ('Open block')
LSWR	Main line to Southampton and on suburban lines. ('Closed block', ie top semaphore's normal position raised.)
GER	London area. Three-position version used showing 'Train accepted' when plunger was operated and 'Train on' when the switch hook was turned over the plunger on receiving 'train on line' from the box in rear.
LTSR	On 'widened lines' between Campbell Road Junction and Barking. Three-position version used.
GSWR	Around Glasgow.
NBR	A few locations.
LDECR	
H&BR	
Mersey Railway	
Wirral Railway	
Liverpool Overhead Railway	The sections between the last two stations at either end of the system.
District Railway	Special version.

release the lock on the plunger if it had to be pressed a second time to unlock the signalbox in rear's section signal; (2) if the section signal had been pulled off, but the train had been cancelled before passing over the releasing treadle, the key had to be used to unlock the lever so that it could be put back fully into the frame. The GER system was so contrived that in the first case the signalman in the rear had to press a button to electrically unlock a shutter across the release keyhole in the advanced instrument. While the shutter was open and the key in the instrument, the circuit between the two signalboxes was broken, removing any risk of the signalman leaving the release key permanently in the instrument. In the second case, the signalman in advance had to press a button to electrically release the 'back-lock' on the rear signalbox's section signal. Co-operation in this way reduced the risk of abuse.

By 1889 there were a number of other fully developed lock and block systems — McKenzie & Holland, Pryce & Ferreira, Saxby & Farmer (Hodgson's Patent), Spagnoletti, and Tyer's. In the 1890s the MR also experimented with its own system, perfecting it in the first decade of the 20th century and finally obtaining a patent for it in 1915 (No 9134). Compared to Sykes equipment, which was completely different from any other form of block instrument, the MR's aim was to incorporate the principles and safeguards of lock and block into as near as possible an existing instrument, making more use of electrical circuitry than mechanical connections between the instrument and lever frame. The resultant instrument could then simply replace the existing single-needle, three-position pegging instrument on the block shelf. Standard block procedures could remain unaltered, and consequently, under normal operating conditions, signalmen did not have to modify their working practices.

The instrument remained unique to the MR, but was widely used by that company. It is also worthy of note because, with one exception (Tyer's three-position, one-wire non-sequential block instrument patented in 1919), it marked the end of the era of patents for individual pieces of electrical equipment specially designed for railway use.

The Positive Legacy

The signalling achievements of all railway companies after 1870 were impressive, and much of the railway infrastructure that was created lasted into the 1960s and 1970s. Many of the lines closed as a result of the Beeching Report of 1963, and the way in which they were operated had not changed for over 80 years.

The Railway Inspectorate

Much of the credit for the signalling 'revolution' lies with the Railway Inspectorate of the Board of Trade. The Inspectorate already had powers under an Act of 1842 to prevent new lines opening if its inspectors were not satisfied with, among other things, the signalling arrangements. These powers of inspection were extended, under the Regulation of Railways Act 1871, to existing lines where alterations had been made. Accidents had to be reported to the Inspectorate, who also had to investigate the causes, make recommendations for improvements and publish the results. A further Act in 1873 required all railways to submit annual returns to the Board of Trade, stating the progress made with interlocking and the block system. Until the Regulation of Railways Act of 1889, the Inspectorate was never able to force railway companies to change their operating practices, adopt new procedures or install specific equipment, but its influence and the steady pressure it exerted in the 1870s undoubtedly led to ever improving standards (see table below).

Of the major British railway companies, the NLR and Metropolitan Railway were fully interlocked by 1875, followed by the LBSCR and NSR by 1880, the Taff Vale by 1881, the LCDR by 1884, the CLC and NER by 1888, the LSWR by 1889, the LNWR by 1890, the MSLR by 1891, the LTSR and the MR by 1892, the CR and GSWR by 1893, and the SER and NBR by 1894.

Rules & Regulations

Standardisation of procedures in operating the block system took as long to achieve as getting it universally adopted, accidents unfortunately being one of the most effective motors of change. Two of the first changes which, with hindsight, can be seen as perhaps the most important breaks with previous procedures, happened because of accidents on the GNR.

As soon as fixed signals had appeared on Britain's railways, they normally displayed a clear indication unless they were protecting a junction or a stationary train, when they were kept at danger. This principle also applied to block working when it was adopted. If there

Percentage of connections on passenger lines interlocked										
year end	1875	1876	1877	1878	1879	1880	1881	1882	1883	1884
England & Wales	63%	69%	73%	77%	80%	82%	85%	87%	88%	90%
Scotland	35%	49%	52%	56%	61%	64%	67%	69%	71%	75%
year end	1885	1886	1887	1888	1889	1890	1891	1892	1893	1894	1895
England & Wales	91%	92%	93%	94%	94%	95%	97%	98%	99%	99%	99%
Scotland	77%	79%	79%	82%	83%	87%	88%	93%	97%	99%	99%

Percentage of double lines worked on Absolute Block System										
year end	1874	1876	1878	1880	1882	1884	1886	1888	1890	1892	1894
England & Wales	63%	78%	83%	89%	93%	95%	97%	97%	98.5%	99.5%	99.8%
Scotland	33%	51%	61%	71%	85%	95%	97.5%	99%	100%	100%	100%

Left (33):
GNR somersault home signal, photographed at Leadenham on the Lincoln-Honington Junction branch in April 1953. R. O. Tuck

Below (34):
A page from the Railway Signal Co's 1909 trade catalogue, illustrating the component parts of a somersault signal.
Transport Trust Library

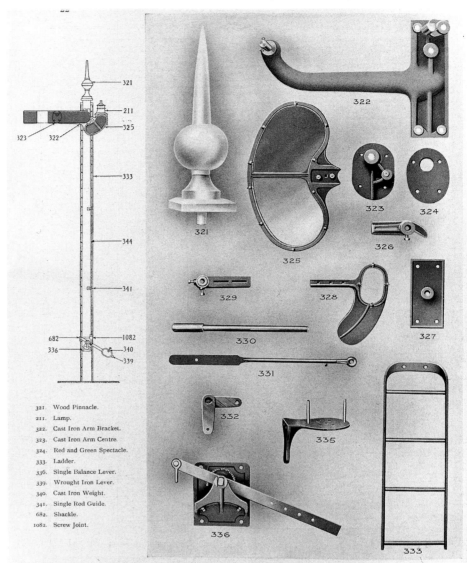

321.	Wood Pinnacle.
211.	Lamp.
322.	Cast Iron Arm Bracket.
323.	Cast Iron Arm Centre.
324.	Red and Green Spectacle.
333.	Ladder.
336.	Single Balance Lever.
339.	Wrought Iron Lever.
340.	Cast Iron Weight.
341.	Single Rod Guide.
682.	Shackle.
1082.	Screw Joint.

were no trains on a line the signals remained at all clear, and the block instruments normally indicated line clear. This became known as open block working (not to be confused with the use of the term by the SR in the 1930s).

At junctions and terminal stations the signals were normally kept in the danger position until a train 'whistled for the signal'. Signals operated in this way formed part of what was known as the 'affirmative' system and there was some debate about its merits. In the East Lancashire Railway's Bye-laws, Rules & Regulations Book of October 1854, drivers had to be reminded to obey all signals, '...whether the cause of the signal is known to them or not, and any engineman neglecting to obey a signal is liable to immediate dismissal...'. But the same Rule (23) went on to state that 'Enginemen must not, however, trust to Signals, but on all occasions be vigilant & cautious...'.

Even in the following decade, when signals became accepted as a necessary control, the affirmative system was still disapproved of by some. An accident on the LSWR at Egham in 1862 was caused by a driver consciously ignoring a signal at danger. The problem of whether the normal indication of signals should be danger or all clear was not fully addressed even after the block system had been generally accepted, and in the early 1870s, semaphores on plain stretches of track with no level crossings or sidings were usually kept in the off position, while at junctions and terminal stations they remained normally on.

Another legacy of the time interval system was the construction of semaphores. In order to be able to display three indications — danger, caution, clear — the arm was pivoted in a slot in the signal post. The clear indication was when the arm was out of sight in the slot, the caution indication when the arm was inclined at 45° and the danger

indication when the arm was horizontal. At junctions only two indications were normally displayed — danger and caution. When block working was adopted, the caution aspect was no longer needed because the line was either clear or not. But semaphore arms continued to be pivoted in slotted posts.

All these elements inherited from pre-block working days together led to the disaster on the night of 21 January 1876, when two expresses piled into a goods train in heavy snow at Abbots Ripton on the GNR main line. The cause was snow packed and frozen into the signal slots, preventing the semaphores, which were of course normally kept in the all clear position, from being put to danger. Following the Railway Inspectorate investigation, the Board of Trade recommended that semaphores should normally be kept at danger until they needed to be pulled off to allow a train into the block section — the affirmative system. All railway companies complied, many altering the use of the block instruments so they too normally

showed line blocked, or if miniature semaphore instruments, with the arms at danger — closed block working.

Gradually, all companies except the NER also redesigned their semaphores to eliminate slotted posts. The GNR went one step further and introduced a signal in which the arm was pivoted on a bracket completely separate from the post. It was the first semaphore to give a positive all clear indication, because the arm remained visible in the clear position. Because of its acrobatic manoeuvre from danger to clear, the new signal was christened a 'somersault', or to the ordinary signalman, a 'tumbler' (Pictures 33 & 34).

The second GNR accident which led to a fundamental change in procedures, occurred in the same year as the Abbots Ripton accident. Until that year, a block section was considered clear if there was no train between the distant signal and the first home signal. The assumption was that a driver seeing a distant signal in the on position, would be able to stop his train before he reached the

31

home signal. Most railwaymen must have known this was not always possible, and in 1874 the MR's engineer had voiced his opinion that it was unsafe to allow a train to approach if another was only just within the protection of the home signal. His comments proved prophetic, because on 23 December 1876 a GNR express, having applied its brake at the distant signal, over-ran the home signal at Arlesey Sidings by 283yd and crashed into goods wagons, killing six people. The lesson was learnt, and the 'clearing point' (or in later years the 'overlap') was added to block working procedures — the line was not considered clear for the approach of a train unless it was unobstructed for 440yd in advance of the first home signal.

The GNR was no more or less accident prone or unsafe than any other main line railway in this period, so it was unfortunate rather than by negligence that another crash on a line linking it with the NLR at Canonbury in 1881 led to further changes in Rules & Regulations. The accident highlighted the dangers of signalmen of different companies misinterpreting bell codes when their signalbox was adjacent to one of another company, and as a result, 17 basic bell codes for signalmen to use in describing the type of train passing between signalboxes and for communicating when emergencies arose, were adopted by all companies right at the end of 1884. Over the next few years, these codes were added to and refined further so that from 3 March 1895, 32 codes and a comprehensive set of 30 standard block regulations issued by the Railway Clearing House (RCH), were brought into use on all Britain's railways (see table on right).

Most of these codes still remain valid where block working is in force today, or where single-stroke block bells are used to communicate between signalmen.

Rule Books were the last important element in procedures to be brought into line. Surprisingly, some of the earliest Rule Books of the 1840s and 50s had much more in common than might be expected. During the following decades, companies did manage to agree on the basics, for the very practical reason that running powers and inter-company working were prevalent all over the country. Eventually, in 1904 the RCH issued 281 standard rules, most railways printing these in their own style of small pocket book, one provided for every employee. From then on, Rules & Regulations were only added to, but not modified, to suit individual companies' needs. Very often, additions to the RCH standards were distinguished in Rules & Regulations Books by the use of italic type. Although most of these 'special' additions had disappeared by nationalisation in 1948, the RCH standard ones remained in force until the 1980s.

The Negative Legacy

Despite the achievements, agreement and degree of standardisation of the years after 1870, certain anomalies and compromises that had arisen in the transition period at the end of the 1860s and the beginning of the 1870s, still remained when they should have been modified or even abandoned.

Three Positions

Rules & Regulations might have been standardised by the beginning of the 20th century, but this was certainly not the case when it came to the electrical equipment for controlling the block system. By then block working was based firmly around three indications — line blocked (line closed or normal), line clear or train on line.

Continuous current needle block instruments using Spagnoletti's patent needle were all capable of displaying these three indications, but there were still thousands of instruments in use all over the country which incorporated miniature semaphore arms or needles which, because they were activated by momentary currents, could only display two indications. Spagnoletti's own design of instrument which remained the standard on the GWR and Metropolitan Railway, could have been made to show three distinct indications but for some inexplicable reason they were never modified. Tyer & Co did patent two three-position, one-wire (momentary current) instruments in 1902 (Patent No 9284) and 1919 (Patent No 126225), but only a few companies took the trouble to convert *(Picture 35)*.

If proof were needed as to how Britain's railways clung far too long to obsolete equipment, then it only needs to be recorded that the last Tyer's two-position semaphore block instruments were taken out of service as recently as January 1990.

Description	No of beats	How sent
Acknowledgment	1	1
Is Line Clear for Express Passenger Train, or Breakdown Van Train going to Clear the Line, or Light Engine going to assist Disabled Train?	4	4
Is Line Clear for Ordinary Passenger Train, or Breakdown? Van Train not going to Clear the Line	4	3 — 1
Is Line Clear for Empty Coaching Stock Train?	5	2 — 2 — 1
Is Line Clear for Express Cattle or Express Goods Train?	5	1 — 4
Is Line Clear for Ordinary Goods or Mineral Train stopping at intermediate Stations?	3	3
Is Line Clear for Branch Goods Train?	3	1 — 2
Is Line Clear for Through Goods, Mineral, or Ballast Train?	5	4 — 1
Is Line Clear for Light Engine, or Light Engines coupled together, or Engine and Brake?	5	2 — 3
Is Line Clear for Ballast Train requiring to stop in Section, Goods Train calling at intermediate Sidings in Section, or Platelayers' Lorry *(sic)* requiring to pass through Tunnel?	5	1 — 2 — 2
Train Entering Section	2	2
Bank Engine in rear of Train	4	2 — 2
Train out of Section or Obstruction removed	3	2 — 1
Obstruction Danger	6	6
Blocking Back	6	3 — 3 (outside Home) 2 — 4 (inside Home)
Stop & Examine	7	7
Take off Slot	7	3 — 4
Cancelling 'Is Line Clear' or 'Train Entering Section'	8	3 — 5
Last Train Signalled incorrectly described	8	5 — 3
Train passed without Tail Lamp	9	9 (to box in advance) 4 — 5 (to box in rear)
Train Divided	10	5 — 5
Train Waiting (or Shunt Train for following Train to pass)	11	1 — 5 — 5
Vehicles running away on Wrong Line (to box in direction in which vehicles are running)	12	2 — 5 — 5
Cancel Bank Engine in rear of Train	12	8 — 2 — 2
Section Clear, but Station or Junction Blocked	13	3 — 5 — 2
Vehicles running away on Right Line (to box in direction in which vehicles are running)	14	4 — 5 — 5
Opening of Signalbox	15	5 — 5 — 5
Testing Instruments	16	16
Closing of Signalbox	17	7 — 5 — 5
Time Signal, 10am	18	8 — 5 — 5
Lampman or Fog Signalman required	19	9 — 5 — 5
Testing Slotted Signals	20	5 — 5 — 5 — 5

White is Right?

The display of a white light at night had emerged as the all clear indication in the 1840s but its continued use was being questioned in the 1870s. Thirty years before, street lighting was unusual and there were very few other nocturnal lights to confuse train drivers. By the 1870s this was no longer the case and in 1873 an accident at Stourbridge that was the result of a driver mistaking a white lamp on the station platform for an all clear signal indication, showed the dangers were real. There was also the risk that if the red coloured glass placed in front of the signal lamp to indicate danger became dislodged and the lamp then showed its natural yellowish flame, the resultant aspect would be interpreted as all clear. This alone made it more sensible to use a white light to indicate danger.

During the 1870s, as the three-position semaphore was abandoned, the green caution aspect became obsolete. A number of people suggested that green should then be adopted to indicate all clear, and one of the first companies to make this change was the GNR after 1876. The Board of Trade did not press the matter, however, and other companies were in no hurry to change. Consequently, for too many years there were two possible all clear aspects, white or green, and on railways where green had been adopted, two possible danger aspects, red or white, the assumption being that if a white light was displayed, there was a fault with the equipment and therefore a driver had to err on the side of safety and stop his train.

There was the real danger of misunderstandings as inter-company running, the speed and frequency of trains increased, and it is amazing that these anomalies should have been tolerated for so many years. It was not until a Railway Clearing House meeting in July 1893 that the recommendation was made that white should be abandoned as an all clear indication and green should be used instead.

The Problem of the Distant Signal

This decision, long overdue, overlooked and by default, confirmed a worse anomaly which had been tolerated for nearly 20 years and after the recommendations of 1893 was to be tolerated for another 30. What emerged from the RCH meeting was the recommendation that only two aspects should be adopted for all running line signals, both stop and distant. During the 1850s-60s, many railway companies had adopted semaphores for their stop signals but continued to use shaped boards for their distant signals. Drivers then had no trouble distinguishing station (home) signals from distant signals *(Picture 36)*. But during the 1870s, semaphores replaced boards altogether on some lines, and for a time distant signals were indistinguishable from stop signals.

Obviously, the standardisation of signals on the semaphore pattern, as far as distant signals was concerned, was a retrogressive step. Then in 1872, the LBSCR began to cut a V-shaped notch out of the end of the distant signal's arm, and from 1876/77 other companies followed that example. But this was an altogether inadequate solution to the problem of identifying the distant signal, whose arm continued to be painted red like stop signals, and whose night-time aspect continued to be exactly the same as stop signals — an anomaly given official sanction after the 1893 RCH meeting.

Amazingly, this anomaly lasted until the 1920s, with only two serious attempts to rectify the situation. The Furness Railway tried a flashing light on some of its distant signals and a number of other companies, most notably the LSWR, employed a device called the Coligny-Welch lamp on its distant signals. By means of an angled mirror inside the lamp case, an external screen adjacent to the lens and just to the right of the spectacle frame at the end of the semaphore arm displayed a white chevron or arrow when the lamp was lit. The 'problem of the distant signal', to use an early 20th century phrase, was not addressed properly until after World War 1.

The Status Quo

By the end of the 19th century the practices developed in the previous 30 years, the Rule & Regulations, the good, the bad and the anomalies, had become ingrained in the minds of all railwaymen from platelayers to directors. The great railway machine worked because the established and accepted procedures were strictly observed. Innovation became as difficult to justify as it had been in the 1860s. The generation of signalmen the author got to know in the 1970s were the direct descendants of those late 19th century railwaymen. Procedures were discussed, questioned, subjected to long debates, certainly. But in the end they were accepted — 'that's the way it's done'. The legacy of the 1870s and 1880s was enormous and long-lasting, and it influenced for better or worse almost all subsequent railway operation for the next 100 years.

Above (37):
The 1870s overhead signalbox at the east end of Newcastle station, photographed at the beginning of extensive track alterations 1893-5. The structure was demolished when the work was complete and replaced by a new 244-lever signalbox.
Newcastle upon Tyne City Libraries & Arts, Local Studies Section

Left (38):
Godalming Junction Signals is the name of this Saxby signalbox photographed in November 1892. The junction was formed in 1859 when the original station at Godalming was bypassed by the opening of the direct Portsmouth line. The box probably opened in the 1860s and was closed when the original station ceased to be used by passengers in 1897. *Surrey Local Studies Library*

3 Power Signalling 1889-1917

The last decade of the 19th century and the first 10 years of the next was a time of both growth and consolidation for Britain's railway companies. The design of locomotives improved; the speed of trains increased; passenger carriages for all classes became more comfortable; and there was much more co-operation between companies, leading, particularly at the turn of the century, to many long distance cross-country services. The increase in passenger and goods traffic drove many railways to re-equip or rebuild their facilities in order to cope with demand.

But business was no longer cut-throat and this fostered a certain complacency in management. There appeared to be enough money to invest in new building. The extension of the MSLR to London in the 1890s is the ultimate example of this belief. Widening schemes were carried out, new goods yards opened and many major stations were completely transformed, often very lavishly. Sheffield MR, Oxford GWR, Reading GWR, Edinburgh Waverley, Crewe, Nottingham MR, Leicester MR, Manchester Victoria L&YR, to name but a few, were all rebuilt in the two decades between 1890 and 1910.

Manual Excess

The end of the Victorian era was also a time of extensive and expensive resignalling schemes. In this period much of the 1860s and early 1870s signalling equipment was replaced *(Pictures 37 & 38)*. Photographs show that a significant amount of this replacement equipment — signal posts, lever frames, block instruments, signal repeaters, etc — lasted well into the 20th century, only being taken out of use when lines closed or routes were modernised after World War 2.

In many ways manual signalling came of age at the end of Queen Victoria's reign and the beginning of her son's. At no other time was there such a variety of mechanical equipment available to the signal engineer. There were numerous designs of semaphore arms, lamps, finials, signal posts, slotting mechanisms, ground signals/disc signals/ shunt signals, facing point locks, point rodding, point rod rollers, point adjusting screws, compensators, detectors, fouling bars, lock bars, pulleys, cranks, signal wire adjusters, level crossing gates, ground frames, not to mention lever frames with interlocking of great sophistication.

In this period the largest mechanical lever frames ever constructed were installed in some of the largest signalboxes ever built. Mechanical installations just seemed to increase in size and complexity. The continuing story of Waterloo A signalbox,

London, illustrates this trend quite clearly. The early signalboxes have been described in the previous chapter. By the 1890s further extensions at the terminus meant the signalling had to be altered again, so another signalbox on the existing gantry was built alongside the existing structure. The operating floor measured 60ft by 30ft and was fitted with a 236-lever Stevens frame, divided into two sections so that the signalmen worked back to back. The first part of the frame was brought into use on 15 May 1892, the 1878/8 signalbox was demolished, and the final connections to the new structure followed a few weeks later. It was claimed that without the installation of special setting levers and locking levers, approximately 400 levers would have been needed to control the station layout. As it was, Major Marindin of the Railway Inspectorate spent three days testing the locking *(Picture 39)*. Further levers were added in 1913, boosting the number to 250, and by the time the signalbox was abolished in October 1936, the total stood at 262.

Across the Thames a frame of 243 levers was brought into use in a new Cannon Street No 1 signalbox on 22 April 1893. At the other end of the country, Edinburgh Waverley station was extensively enlarged between 1892 and 1899, and four new signalboxes were erected to control the new layout and the 1,000 trains and engines working at, or passing through, the station every day. Waverley East,

which opened on 11 July 1898, was the largest, fitted with a 260-lever Railway Signal Co frame *(Picture 40)*. Reading station was resignalled in 1896, when two new signalboxes were erected, the East box fitted with a 115-lever frame and the West box with 185 — the latter replaced in February 1912 by a 222-lever frame *(Picture 41)*.

In 1903-5 Shrewsbury station was resignalled, Severn Bridge Junction equipped with 180 levers and Crewe Junction with 120, both frames of standard LNWR tumbler design. In 1907, Liverpool Street West was equipped with two back to back McKenzie & Holland frames of 120 and 124 levers each *(Picture 42)* and barely two years later the same Worcester firm manufactured and installed in Locomotive Yard, York, a mechanical frame with the highest number of levers — 295 — in one continuous row anywhere in the world. The first section of this enormous frame was brought into use on 6 June 1909, and once the signalbox it replaced had been demolished, the new signalling was fully commissioned two weeks later. Initially 43 levers were spare (ie not in

Below (39):
Waterloo A signalbox was only two months old when this photograph was taken on 23 July 1892. *Public Record Office*

Above (40):
Ex-GNR 4-4-0 No 3063 passing Edinburgh Waverley West signalbox in the 1920s. Waverley West, the smaller of the two main boxes brought into use at the end of the 1890s, contained a frame of only 205 levers manufactured and installed by the Railway Signal Co.
D. J Powell Collection

Right (41):
The operating floor of Reading Main Line West signalbox photographed in the 1920s. *Real Photographs*

use), but after alterations in 1911, this number was reduced to only 17 *(Picture 43)*.

However, it was not just the major traffic centres that kept the signalling contractors in business in this period. The 1889 Regulation of Railways Act made interlocking and the use of the block system compulsory on all passenger lines. The last pockets of primitive signalling were systematically re-equipped to conform to the requirements of the Act, resulting in hundreds of installations where the level of passenger and goods service and the revenue return from them was hardly sufficient to cover the capital costs of providing the signalling. The MSLR's 26 miles of double track between Claytons Siding signalbox, Lincoln, and Howsham, just south of Wrawby Junction (Barnetby), was still worked on the time interval system at the end of the 1880s. In 1890 a dozen signalboxes were brought into use, with a combined total of almost 250 levers *(Picture 44)*. The same happened on many other branch lines, and all over the country lightly used railways were provided with signalling equipment more up to date and comprehensive than on the overburdened main lines *(Picture 45)*.

At the end of the 19th century the MR boasted it had 1,682 signalboxes with 19,240 levers working 13,403 signals. In comparison the LNWR estimated it had 1,500 signalboxes with a total of 36,200 levers in use, working a reported 14,500 signals. The GWR's total of signals was said to be 12,500 and the L&YR's 11,500. The latter company claimed that its drivers passed an average of 22 signals every mile, far more than the GWR with an average of only five per mile or the MR with twice that many.

All these statistics pleased many engineers and reassured the public that progress was inevitably being made. But they also convinced other more progressive engineers that an alternative to manual power was required. The longer the lever frame and the more levers that needed to be pulled or pushed to set up a route for the passage of a train, the more time it took for a signalman to set that route.

In manual installations, lineside equipment had to be connected to the levers operating them in the signalbox by sturdy rods, cranks, wires, pulleys and chains, all of which had to be very carefully installed and adjusted for trouble-free operation. The more equipment, the more connecting ironmongery was needed. This took up more and more valuable space at major stations and junctions, restricting the way lines could be laid out and presenting a hazard to men working at track level, a consideration that managers were forced to take seriously following the Railway Employment (Prevention of Accidents) Act of 1900 and associated Rules of 1902.

The routing of signal wires and point rodding between levers and signals could become convoluted, making a signalman's job more strenuous *(Picture 46)*. The more difficult the route and the further away the equipment was from the lever, the more compensating weights had to be attached to the tails of the levers to aid the signalman when pulling them. This added to the forces of compression when the lever was thrust back in the frame, and the busier the signalbox the less time the signalmen had to worry about how roughly he treated those levers. The pulling and pushing of levers many thousands of times a day, the rubbing of metal against metal, the expansion and contraction of signal wires, the movement of semaphore arms up and down, the continual wear and tear no matter how well lubricated, meant every mechanical installation needed continual maintenance and periodic renewal of parts.

Power

The solution to the problems of conveying power mechanically from the lever to the point or signal was to place the means of

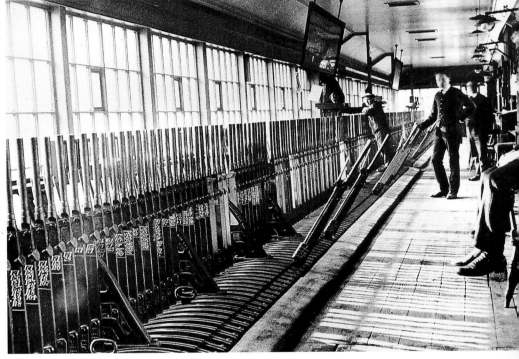

Left (42):
Liverpool Street station photographed on 8 August 1911, with Skinner Street bridge in the background and Broad Street No 2 signalbox beyond. Of note are the miniature repeater (co-acting) semaphores at the base of the bracket to the right of the photograph.
National Railway Museum (GE854)

Above right (43):
Part of the 295-lever frame inside Locomotive Yard, York. *National Railway Museum*

Right (44):
Moortown signalbox, opened in 1890 on the MSLR's Lincoln to Wrawby Junction (Barnetby) line, contained a frame of 23 levers and was only a few years old when this photograph was taken. The signalbox remained in use until 16 April 1989.
National Railway Museum

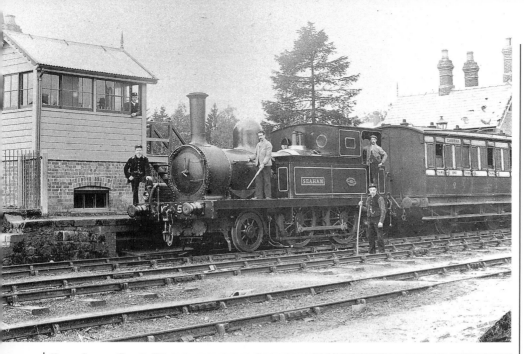

signal engineers, including two home grown varieties:

i)   Westinghouse — an electro-pneumatic system first used in America in 1892, its production in this country licensed by the Westinghouse Brake Co in London to McKenzie & Holland in 1895.
ii) British Pneumatic Railway Signal Co — an all-pneumatic or low-pressure compressed air system developed in North America.
iii) Bianchi & Servettaz — a hydraulic system used in Italy and southern France, the patent rights taken up in this country by Saxby & Farmer in 1890.
iv) Siemens & Halske of Berlin and Vienna — an all-electric system widely used in Germany and Austria after 1894 and marketed in this country by the sister firm of Siemens Bros.
v)   Hall Automatic Signal Co — an all-electric system developed in the USA.
vi) Webb & Thompson — an all-electric system developed by the LNWR Signal Department, licensed to the Railway Signal Co for installation on other railways, but with one exception used exclusively on LNWR lines.
vii) W. R. Sykes Interlocking Signal Co — an electro-mechanical system where the signals were electrically operated and the points worked from a standard mechanical lever frame.

It is probably fair to say that power signalling became a fad, or to quote a contemporary article, was 'in vogue', in this country in the first decade of the 20th century and the years leading up to World War 1. The sudden extension of the London Underground — the new 'tube' railways — relying on electric traction, power and automatic signalling, combined with the success of the new electric tram systems in many large cities, affected even the old established main line railway companies, sweeping many of their engineering staff along in a wave of enthusiasm for all things new. For a short time, even main line electrification seemed a real possibility, the LSWR and LBSCR demonstrating what could be achieved with suburban services and the NER for goods traffic.

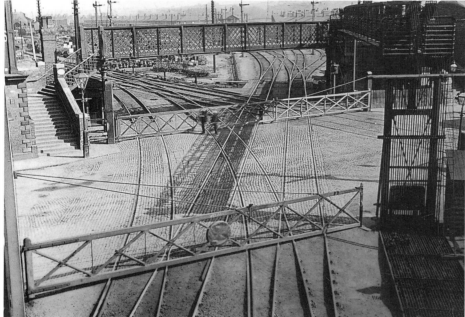

power next to the piece of equipment it had to operate. The connection between lever and equipment then became static, its route less critical to mechanical efficiency, and the lever could become no more than a switch to turn the power source on and off. As the lever then played no part in the transmission of mechanical power, it could be miniaturised, or replaced by other handles or slides, and consequently power frames took up far less space than traditional mechanical lever frames. Signalmen could spend less time walking up and down long frames, expending their energy on pulling levers, and concentrate on pure signalling — the margining of trains, etc.

The idea of using other than mechanical power transmission was not new. Perhaps the earliest suggestion was embodied in a patent granted to James Stevens in 1847 (No 11612). Included in the specification was a closed-circuit pneumatic arrangement with a sack at either end of a long rubber tube. The idea was that when one sack was compressed between

two plates by the signalman, it caused the other sack at the other end of the tube to inflate, pushing the rod of the distant signal and thereby pushing the signal to the all clear position. When the signalman removed the pressure, the distant signal was counter-weighted to return to danger.

Needless to say, Stevens' device was not put to any practical use, nor were most of the other ideas made in an era when mechanical equipment was the unquestioned technology. The prejudices were not overcome until a new generation of engineers looked afresh at the possibilities. The first practical application of other than mechanical power was in North America, where George Westinghouse carried out experiments in 1884, gradually refining his systems until settling on an electro-pneumatic one in 1892. There were also contemporary developments in Europe, some systems relying on hydraulics, some on compressed air, others on electricity, and by the end of the century there were seven systems available commercially to British

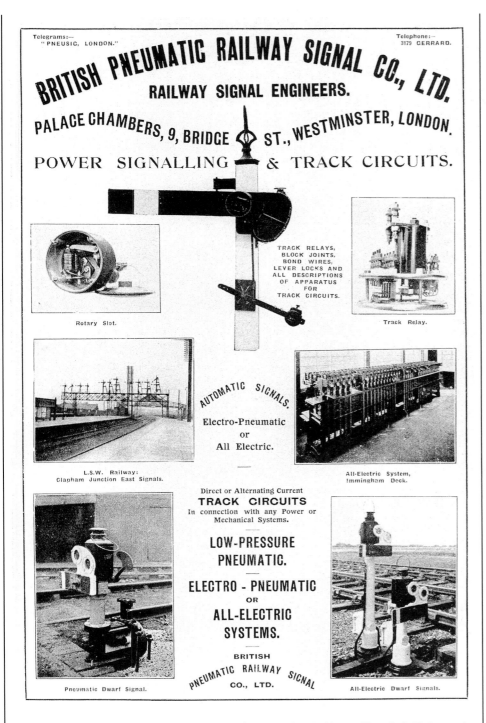

signalling practice (see next chapter). The IRSE was a symptom of the more technical and broader approach to signalling, which by the end of the period covered by this chapter was no longer an art but a science.

Hydraulic Systems

This form of power signalling did not find favour in this country, due mainly to the problems of winter freezing, and there was only one notable example of its use. This was a most ungainly installation at Stobcross East signalbox on the Glasgow Central Low Level line opened in 1896. There were in effect two signalboxes next to each other. The signalman worked from the box which contained a frame of miniature levers and a view of the passing trains. These miniature levers were connected hydraulically to full size mechanical counterparts in an adjacent frame, which actually worked the signals and points from the other unmanned signalbox.

Pneumatic and Electro-Pneumatic Systems

Stobcross East was an isolated and not very successful example and contributed very little to the development of mainstream power signalling. With hindsight we can say that that mainstream was the all-pneumatic/low-pressure or electro-pneumatic system.

The pioneering electro-pneumatic installation, a Westinghouse example, was brought into use by the GER on 15 January 1899 at Spitalfields (Bishopsgate) goods station. Whitechapel signalbox (usually referred to by its later name, Granary Junction) was fitted with a 'table interlocker' (frame) actually imported from the USA. Air was piped to the signals and points from a power house with two compressors. The main pipes were 2in diameter, reducing to ¾in to serve cylinders at the bottom of the signalposts or at the points. The valves to allow air into the cylinders, to operate the piston to move the points or signals, were opened and closed by electro-magnets, which is why the system was described as electro-pneumatic. The operation of the valves was controlled from the table interlocker.

The handles on this type of frame looked like old-fashioned motor car starting handles and were arranged along the front of the frame in a similar way. To operate a point the knob on the handle was turned, so that the handle could be moved to its first intermediate position. A current passed to the electro-magnet at the point, to open the valve to allow air into the cylinder. Once the blades had moved and, if it was a facing point, they had been locked in position, a return current pushed the handle to its fully reversed position. If for any reason the point blades were not proved to have closed properly, no reverse current flowed, the handle remained in its intermediate position and the interlocking in the frame was not freed for any conflicting handles to be operated.

But power signalling was expensive, one contemporary report claiming that installing a Westinghouse electro-pneumatic frame cost the equivalent of £100 a lever compared to between £35 and £50 per lever in a mechanical installation. And although the examples of power signalling on Britain's main lines were all impressive, they made little difference to the operation of the majority of the country's railway network. What developments there might have been were cut short by World War 1, and when resignalling work started again in the 1920s, the direction taken was fundamentally different (Picture 47).

Although the fad was over, what is truly important about the prewar period is the fact it fostered a more technical — scientific if you like — approach to railway signalling. In

1909 The Railway Signal & Telegraphy Engineering Institute was formed as a debating society, and the following year, the Institution of Signal Engineers was established, giving those responsible for signalling on the country's railways the opportunity to meet together and discuss topics of mutual interest. Two years later the latter organisation was reformed into the Institution of Railway Signal Engineers (IRSE), and its worth can be judged from not only the quality of the papers presented at its meetings, but also the practical influence it had on the development of signalling in this country. After World War 1 it was a committee of the IRSE which recommended the most radical change in railway signalling since the introduction of the block system, one which still remains the basis of modern

The action from moving the handle on the frame to the moving of the semaphore arm or point was almost instantaneous. What was also possible with Westinghouse's system was the selection of signals depending on the position of points. This meant one handle could control a number of different signals, the lie of the points 'selecting' which signal responded to the handle.

After the GER experiment the American table interlocker was not used again in this country, but in the space of just 10 years between 1901 and 1911 there were a number of quite complex electro-pneumatic and purely pneumatic or low-pressure installations brought into use all over the country.

The first low-pressure or purely pneumatic system was commissioned in October 1901 at Grateley on the LSWR's line between Salisbury and Andover *(Picture 48)*. In the all-pneumatic system, instead of an electric current opening the valves in the cylinders at the individual points and signals, air flowed down a pipe from the signalbox to a 'relay valve' next to the item of lineside equipment. Air from a reservoir then operated the piston within the cylinder to drive the point blades or semaphore arm.

At Grateley a new signalbox was built to the company's latest design and fitted with a frame of pull-out handles or slides, supplied by the British Pneumatic Railway Signal Co (BPRS). The company had been set up at the end of 1900 by J. P. O'Donnell of Evans, O'Donnell, the mechanical signalling contractor, and this type of frame became the standard for a number of pneumatic, electro-pneumatic and, in a slightly altered form, for all-electric installations.

The majority of slides operated individual pieces of lineside equipment, but there were a few pairs of ground signals operated by just one slide, the lie of the points selecting which signal responded to the slide. The handles of each slide were colour-coded to indicate the type of equipment they controlled, the colours corresponding with those used for mechanical lever frames; red for stop signals, black for points. As with the Whitechapel installation, a point had to prove it had responded correctly to the pulling of the slide, before air pushed it automatically to its fully reversed position, thus freeing the interlocking for the next slide to be operated. The air pressure in the valves for working points or signals was $7\frac{1}{2}$ psi, reduced down from 15psi in the connecting main.

The LSWR and the Board of Trade were satisfied with the reliability of the Grateley installation, and the following year, as part of the rebuilding of Salisbury station, the railway company resignalled the new track

Above (50):
A Reading train passing under Clapham Junction East signalbox on 27 July 1926. By then the box had been redesignated Clapham Junction A by the new SR.
H. C. Casserley/D. J. Powell Collection

Right (51):
The L&YR's official photograph of the power frame inside Bolton West signalbox on 18 February 1912. Clearly visible are a number of miniature levers standing upright so they can serve a dual function, depending on whether they are pulled forward or pushed back in the frame. All the instruments with sloping fronts on the block shelf are standard Tyer permissive block instruments, while the three at the far end of the shelf are the L&YR's own design of double line absolute block instruments.
National Railway Museum (HORF966)

layout and controlled it from two signalboxes fitted with BPRS Co frames. Both contained 64 slides and were commissioned in November 1902. Just under a year later, two new signalboxes with the same equipment with a total of 72 slides were opened at Staines and this was followed by the equipping of 12 signalboxes on the 24 miles of track between Woking Junction and Basingstoke with BPRS Co frames. At Basingstoke two new boxes, the East with 45 slides and the West with 55, took over the work of three mechanical ones in 1906. On the same stretch of quadruple line there were a number of sections controlled by automatic signals, the operation of which is described later.

The following year the LSWR built a new overhead signalbox at Clapham Junction (later known as Clapham Junction A), in preparation for the installation of low-pressure pneumatic signalling. Three other traditionally-styled signalboxes were constructed for the same scheme, Clapham Junction West (Main) opening on 21 May 1911, followed by Clapham Junction West (Windsor) (which had been ready since 1907) on 27 May *(Picture 49)*. The overhead

Clapham Junction East was brought into use at the beginning of 1912, equipped with a total of 84 slides *(Picture 50)* and West London Junction, with 48 slides, completed the scheme.

Meanwhile at the other end of England, further Westinghouse electro-pneumatic equipment activated from frames of miniature levers had been installed by McKenzie & Holland for the NER at Tyne Docks Coal Yard in 1902, and by the Westinghouse Brake Co for the L&YR at its new Bolton station in 1903. (The frame used at the latter was an American one with the addition of miniature levers to satisfy the British specification.) The Bolton installation, brought into use on 27 September 1903, was, like so many resignalling schemes of this period, part of the rebuilding and enlargement of the station. J. T. Lawrence, writing in the May 1904 edition of the *Railway Magazine*, was apparently impressed with the new signalbox

with its frame of 77 miniature levers, and wrote:

'Instead of a couple of men stripped to the waist and perspiring from every pore, as the whole weight of the body is thrown on to a lever actuating a quarter of a mile of steel rods and angle irons, we have one man, the weight of whose finger and thumb on a miniature lever about 4in in height, does the same amount of work, the steel rods being replaced by the same length of tubing in which compressed air performs the duty'.

Obviously, Mr Lawrence exercised a certain amount of poetic licence, as it seems unlikely that the L&YR management would have tolerated half-naked signalmen, even in Bolton! *(Picture 51)*.

The GCR was the next company to experiment with electro-pneumatic equipment, using it for the resignalling of the widened lines outside Manchester between Ardwick and Newton. The Ardwick scheme

Left (52):
Audenshaw Junction looking east, with the LNWR line between Ashton Moss and Droylsden junctions immediately behind the signal gantry. For better sighting, the home signals are all co-acting, although the distant signal arms of Stockport Junction are not duplicated.
John Ryan Collection/J. A. Peden (C5426)

Below left (53):
The signal gantries and electro-pneumatically operated semaphores protecting the approaches to Hull Paragon station. *LNER*

new power signalling technology following its first tentative experiment in Tyne Docks in 1902. This was both surprising, as the company was keen on very large and complex fully-mechanical installations, and understandable, given the NER's particularly generous provision of semaphores at major stations and junctions, involving much lever pulling and time-consuming walking up and down very long lever frames.

In 1904, two years after the work on the Tyne, Hull Paragon station and its approaches were resignalled, the station box fitted with a Westinghouse Type B frame of 179 miniature levers, and Park Street equipped with another with 143 miniature levers. The operating technology might have been new, but the semaphores — of which there were a great number — were still the traditional wooden slotted-post variety and still mounted on McKenzie & Holland's impressive but over-engineered metal lattice gantries *(Picture 53)*.

Further electro-pneumatic signalboxes were brought into use on Tyneside in 1905, and the success there and at Hull convinced the NER that Newcastle could be more effectively signalled electro-pneumatically.

Between 1893 and 1895 the eastern approaches to the station had already been remodelled and resignalled, the new layout controlled from a new mechanical signalbox equipped with a 244-lever frame *(Picture 54)*. This box was superseded in 1909 by another, suspended over the tracks and fitted with a 198-miniature lever frame to work electro-pneumatically-operated points and signals. The reduction in the number of levers is interesting, as the signalling was as complex as before. Almost every running signal had a 'calling-on' miniature semaphore beneath it. Unlike other companies, the NER's regulations required the calling-on signal to be off if the main signal above it was off. Sensibly, therefore, both arms in the new installation were controlled from the same lever. The calling-on arm operated when the lever was pulled to an intermediate position in its stroke and both arms cleared to the off position when the lever was fully reversed.

It is very interesting to remember that in the same year as the 'modern' Newcastle No 1 signalbox opened, McKenzie & Holland was equipping Locomotive Yard box at York with 295 traditional mechanical levers. The November 1911 edition of the *Railway*

was a bold move for the company, which had no previous experience with power signalling. Fourteen new signalboxes were erected between 1904 and 1906 and equipped with BPRS Co frames with a total of 463 slides. Dewsnap Sidings signalbox was the first to open on 21 May 1905 *(Picture 52)*. For facing points there were no separate facing point lock slides, the action of one slide putting into motion the unlocking, moving and bolting of the blades. As with other installations, once the blades were proved fully locked against the rail, a reverse indication completed the stroke of the slide in the frame. Certain 'routing' signals were selected according to the position of the points. Each signal was returned to the on position by the train occupying a track circuit in advance of it, and there were no slides to

operate the distant signals, these clearing automatically if all relevant stop signals were off.

The signal engineer responsible for the GCR work was A. F. Bound, who was to make his mark on post-World War 1 British railway signalling history (see next chapter). The low-pressure signalling was finally extended into the GCR's half of Manchester London Road (now Piccadilly) in 1909. Its new station signalbox was built within shouting distance of the LNWR one equipped with that company's 'all-electric system' which controlled its section of the terminus. Both boxes, and the signalling, lasted until the end of 1960, when a new powerbox was opened (see Chapter 5).

As well as the LSWR and the GCR, the NER also showed considerable faith in the

Right (54):
The east end of Newcastle station showing the signal gantry erected as part of the 1893/5 remodelling. This gantry was retained in the resignalling of 1909, and the new overhead electro-pneumatic signalbox was built across and above the lines between the standing man and the lamp post next to the departing train.
Newcastle upon Tyne City Libraries & Arts, Local Studies Section

Below right (55):
Park Lane Junction signalbox, just to the west of Gateshead East station south of the Tyne. An official BR(NE) photograph taken on 6 October 1961.
Fastline Photographic, York (145137)

Magazine devoted a whole article to the new signalbox, and mention was made as to why the NER did not adopt electro-pneumatic signalling at York. All companies agreed that the initial cost of power signalling was always higher than traditional mechanical work, but could be justified by subsequent savings. At York it was calculated that this would not be the case. According to the *Railway Magazine* article, power signalling had been adopted at Newcastle partly because space for large mechanical signalboxes was not available, whereas at York this was not a problem and consequently the NER decided to build a manual signalbox there.

The work at Newcastle was part of a complete resignalling scheme both north and south of the Tyne, precipitated by the opening on 10 July 1906 of the new King Edward Bridge over the river. No 1 signalbox at the east end of the station has just been mentioned; No 2, with a frame of 67 miniature levers, was in the centre of the station; while No 3, with 211 miniature levers operated by three signalmen and two booking lads, was at the west end, situated at the north of the new bridge. The signal gantry at this end of the station carried 57 arms on 25 posts. Five other electro-pneumatic signalboxes with miniature lever frames were provided at King Edward Bridge, Greensfield, High Street, Park Lane Junction (*Picture 55*) and Manors, the last two being erected over the running lines. The signalboxes and gantries remained very impressive features at Newcastle until the resignalling of 1959 and 1962.

The same conversion to electro-pneumatic signalling for a major station happened on the Caledonian Railway at the turn of the century. In 1879 the company opened the new Central station in Glasgow north of the Clyde. This was extended in 1889 and again in 1906, when three manual signalboxes were built. However, barely two years later one new electro-pneumatic signalbox with 374 miniature levers (Westinghouse B) was substituted, erected between the 1879 and 1889 bridges over the river. When the new Central box opened on 3 May 1908, it was the largest power frame ever constructed (*Picture 56*) and it retained that record until it closed on 2 January 1961.

The last electro-pneumatic installation in this country was brought into use at Southport on the L&YR in 1917. A Westinghouse type B frame with 87 miniature levers was used, some of the levers controlling two items of lineside equipment, depending on whether they were pushed or pulled from their normal position of upright (half-way through their normal stroke) in the frame (*Picture 57*).

All-Electric Systems

By the time the installation at Southport was commissioned, it was old-fashioned, and all-electric systems were the progressive answer to resignalling problems. Although at first it might be assumed that the use of electricity naturally followed pneumatic technology, chronologically the two overlapped, and all-electric systems in this country were actually contemporary with other power installations. In fact the credit for bringing into use the first successful power signalling equipment in this country must go to the LNWR, with its all-electric system.

In the 1890s, Crewe station was enlarged and considerable modifications made to the approach lines. It was obvious that power signalling was the most efficient way to control the new complex layouts, and the company approached the Westinghouse firm for an evaluation, as well as purchasing electro-pneumatic and hydraulic equipment for testing purposes.

As might be expected, the LNWR soon decided to design and manufacture all its own equipment and in May 1897 F. W. Webb and A. M. Thompson of the company took out a

Above (56):
The 374-miniature lever frame in Glasgow Central signalbox, photographed shortly after it was brought into use in 1908.
National Railway Museum (SRX386)

Below (57):
An electro-pneumatic point motor (the cylinder) and lock bars at Southport. The point blades could only be moved if no vehicle was standing on the lock bars, so the first movement of the piston in the cylinder pulled or pushed over the bars and the final stroke moved the point blades. On this particular point there are two bars, so there is an extra detector (the rectangular box) next to the cylinder.
National Railway Museum (HORF2912)

joint patent for an all-electric system (No 12128). The LNWR already had an electricity generating station at Crewe and this obviously influenced the choice of power. The signalbox equipment consisted of a frame of miniature levers, which could be arranged in two tiers. The interlocking was the standard tappet type. As in the pneumatic systems described above, the point levers had a 'check-lock' position, the signalman being unable to reverse or put back a lever fully until the lineside equipment had responded correctly and a return current had released the lever lock. Signals were of the standard company pattern but lit by electric lamps and the arms were held in the off position by the

drive motor running at a reduced voltage *(Picture 58)*.

Gresty Lane Sidings, Crewe, was the first signalbox fitted with the new equipment and it opened in December 1898 *(Picture 59)*, just before the GER's Whitechapel (Granary Junction) electro-pneumatic signalbox. The LNWR equipment was soon christened the 'Crewe System' and by 1907 there were nine all-electric signalboxes at that junction, the largest being the North box with 266 miniature levers, closely followed by the South box with 247. Other installations followed at Euston and Camden *(Picture 60)*, and in 1908/9, the company's half of Manchester London Road station was resignalled and three new signalboxes erected with all-electric frames *(Picture 61)*. The only installation outside the LNWR was at Severus Junction on the NER, opened in 1903.

Like the LNWR, the MR and GWR were manufacturing all their own mechanical signalling equipment by the end of the 19th century, but both companies turned to the Siemens firm for their first experiments with power signalling. The British arm of the German company was Siemens Bros & Co Ltd and on 2 April 1905 one of its miniature lever frames was brought into use in the MR's Way & Works signalbox at Derby. It remained the company's only excursion into the new technology.

On 16 July 1905 the GWR brought into use its first power signalling installation, in a new signalbox at Didcot North Junction. Two existing signalboxes were abolished, the GWR being able to work all the points from

Left (58):
Signal gantry at Crewe showing the cylinders containing the solenoid motors beneath the spectacles.
Historical Model Railway Society Photograph Collection/J. P. Richards Collection

Below left (59):
Gresty Lane signalbox, Crewe, photographed on 21 February 1899 when still new. As with traditional lever frames, the locking was beneath the operating floor. The signalman has his left hand on the commutator of a double line permissive block instrument manufactured by Tyer & Co, while at the other end of the block shelf is an example of the LNWR's first style of standard instrument, production of which had begun in the company's Stockport works in 1895.
National Railway Museum (Crewe C625)

The GWR used Siemens equipment again at Birmingham, when Snow Hill station was considerably enlarged and rebuilt between 1909 and 1912. The North signalbox opened on 31 October 1909, fitted with a frame of 224 miniature levers *(Pictures 62-4).* Various improvements on the Didcot equipment were made, some of the locking in the frame being electrical rather than purely mechanical, and standard GWR point parts were modified to work electrically. The South box opened in 1913, shortly after the rebuilt station had been completed.

While the work at Birmingham was in hand, the GWR turned to the McKenzie Holland & Westinghouse Power Signalling Co for two new installations at Yarnton and Slough. At the former a frame of 50 miniature levers was brought into use on 13 June 1909, and four years later a similar one with 23 miniature levers was brought into use at Bath Road Junction, Slough, as a trial to assess whether the company should install all-electric power signalling at Paddington.

The GCR continued to patronise the British Pneumatic Railway Signal Co and in 1911/12 it brought into use six new signalboxes at Immingham Docks, all fitted with the contractor's standard frames of slides but adapted for all-electric working. Next to each signalbox a generator house was erected to provide the 110V supply. The largest frame with 89 slides was fitted in Immingham Reception Sidings box. As with an electro-pneumatic frame, a slide could not be pulled or pushed to its full extent until the piece of lineside equipment had proved to have responded correctly. Then a return current pushed or pulled the slide to its fully reversed or normal position in the frame, thus freeing the mechanical tappet interlocking. Signal arms were pushed to the off position, but returned to danger by gravity.

Electro-Mechanical Systems

At the end of the 1890s, the GSWR approached W. R. Sykes to provide shunting signals for Glasgow St Enoch station. Sykes designed both the control equipment for the

the new box by taking advantage of the Board of Trade's relaxation of the distance that power-operated facing points could be from a signalbox — 300yd instead of 200yd for manually-worked equipment. All points and signals were operated by electric motors, the GWR having erected a building next to the signalbox to house the accumulators. A 'control current' held the signals in the off position, but as soon as this was interrupted, either when the lever was put back to normal in the frame or when a fault occurred, the weight of the arm and spectacle returned the signal to danger. This was obviously also a fail-safe feature — no current for whatever reason always meant the arms returned to, or stayed at, danger. If signals had to be returned to danger in an emergency, there was one switch in the signalbox that could be used to interrupt the current to all signals.

The frame of miniature levers was designed by Luis de Moraz Gomez Ferreira of the Siemens company, who worked with the GWR again, patenting with that railway's Chief Assistant Signal Engineer, in 1918, the first British route-setting equipment (see next chapter). At Didcot the frame had 38 miniature levers, standing a few inches proud of the top of the cabinet containing the electrics and mechanical locking. In front of each lever were two indicators, the top one displaying either 'locked' or 'free' and the bottom one showing the position of the points or signals. The point levers had no check-lock position; in other words they could be fully reversed in one continuous movement, but the electrical circuitry did not free the relevant signal until the point had proved to have responded correctly and a current returned from the point to the interlocking.

Left (60):
Camden No 1 signalbox, fitted with a 'Crewe System' frame of 52 miniature levers, was opened in July 1905. The small size of the structure illustrates the space that was saved when power signalling was adopted. Photographed in June 1939, just a year before it was replaced. *D. J. Powell Collection*

Below (61):
Ex-LMS 'Patriot' No 45520 leaving Manchester London Road on 26 February 1953. On the left-hand side of the gantry in the background are 10 LNWR electrically-operated semaphores, while next to them on the same gantry are three pneumatically-operated GCR lower quadrants. *Brian Green*

Right (62):
Birmingham Snow Hill North signalbox, photographed on 9 September 1960, just two days before it was closed.
BR(W)/D. J Powell Collection

Far right (63):
The interior of Birmingham Snow Hill North signalbox as it appeared just after World War 2.
P. J. Garland Collection/R. S. Carpenter/ D. J. Powell Collection

Below right (64):
One of the signal brackets at Snow Hill station. Standard GWR semaphore arms were used, those with two holes controlling 'wrong line' or 'backing' movements. *Author's Collection*

signalbox and a new type of signal, which came into use on 3 July 1898. The shunting signals took the form of a glazed circular disc 2ft 6in in diameter with a red banner pivoted centrally. At night the unit was illuminated from behind so that it gave the same indications in daylight and in the dark.

The banner was operated electrically, and when inclined from bottom left to top right indicated 'in or out shunt on up line', and when inclined bottom right to top left indicated 'in or out shunt on down line'. These shunting signals were worked from switches in the signalbox, which meant the existing mechanical frame did not have to be enlarged or replaced. To operate one of the shunting signals positioned under a stop signal, the signalman, after setting the route, pulled the stop signal lever forward in the frame only a few inches. He then turned a switch above the lever either to the left or right depending on the indication he wished the shunting signal to display. This action locked the stop signal lever in position to prevent any further movement, and the signalman then pressed a key to activate the shunting signal. Some of the signals were returned to danger as soon as the train passed over a treadle which activated Sykes 'signal reversers'.

The W. R. Sykes Interlocking Signal Co produced a modified version of its banner signal to make its indications clearer and the firm patented the new design in 1909 (No 6145). It was soon put to use as a repeater signal for semaphores on running lines that might be obscured by bridges or station buildings and this role gave it its more familiar name — the banner repeater.

The GSWR returned to the Sykes company again in 1902 when St Enoch station was being extended, and installed in the new signalbox there that firm's distinctive lock & block electro-mechanical signalling apparatus. This had been patented by W. R. Sykes Jnr in 1901 (No 7067). The new equipment incorporating lock and block instruments and a row of slides to operate the signals electrically was fitted over a traditional mechanical frame of 88 levers for operating the points. After the points had been moved to set a particular route, a 'routing' or 'key' lever was reversed or put back to the normal position in the frame, depending on the route to be signalled, which unlocked the signal slides. Facing point lock levers were dispensed with and point levers were electrically locked while a train passed over them. The reduction in the number of mechanical levers required was therefore quite marked and, although the layout at St Enoch had been enlarged, the 88 levers in the new frame compared favourably with the 117 in the old box. Four other new signalboxes on the approaches to the station were similarly equipped with Sykes electro-mechanical equipment. St Enoch signalbox survived until replaced in May 1933 *(Picture 65)*.

Sykes electro-mechanical equipment was used again by the CR at Dalry, and to a greater extent by the SECR to control the Grove Park widenings *(Picture 66)* and at Folkestone, and by the LBSCR at Victoria station after the extensive alterations there in 1908. Three signalboxes were involved in this resignalling scheme, the largest, Victoria South, containing 106 mechanical levers and 163 electrical slides. Almost all the platform starting signals were Sykes banner signals illuminated at night by gaslight.

Automatic Signalling

Before the block system had become the standard way of controlling trains, a number of attempts had been made to eliminate the human element by devising ways in which the trains themselves could operate the signals. In the 1850s, Edward Tyer had experimented, and in 1864 a Mr Funnell carried out trials of his own equipment on the LBSCR, whereby once a train had passed one signal and the indication had automatically been altered to danger, it completed an electrical circuit which operated the signal in rear — one section behind the train — altering it to all clear. Other attempts were made by other inventors, but by 1874, R. Rapier in his paper 'On the Fixed Signals of Railways' echoed a belief that was held for many years, that there were not sufficient uninterrupted stretches of track in Britain to make the introduction of automatic signalling worth while. It was not until that generation of signal engineers had retired, that the benefits of automatic signalling could be objectively reassessed.

As with other innovations such as power signalling, automatic signalling had been successfully brought into common use for the first time in the USA. Its use in Britain was delayed for a number of reasons, the most important of which was signal engineers' prejudice against track circuiting, on which automatic signalling relied. In this country the first form of automatic signalling had been brought into use without the use of track circuits on the Liverpool Overhead Railway in 1893, but it was obvious such a system could not be adapted for use on main line railways. Track circuiting was the only answer.

Put very simply, a track circuit was (and is) a relay and a battery connected to each other by the rails of a section of track. When the wheels of a train interrupted the current, the relay being de-energised could form or break another circuit to another item of equipment — an indicator in the signalbox, or the motor of a signal. This simple principle had long been understood, but it was not accepted as a reliable addition to signal engineering until the first decade of the 20th century. Among the many problems that had to be overcome before it was fully accepted, was one caused by the use of Mansell wheels with wooden centres, which very effectively insulated axles from the tyres touching the track. This problem was overcome by making a physical metal link between tyre and axle, a modification that all railway companies were required to make after 1908.

The first track circuits to be used to control automatic signals formed part of the LSWR's 1901 Grateley scheme. A number of

automatic, low-pressure, pneumatically-operated signals were brought into use between there and Andover Junction in the spring of 1902. The reliability of this installation persuaded the company to invest in a truly impressive scheme on the 24-mile stretch of quadruple track between Woking Junction and Basingstoke a few years later.

Every automatic signal was provided with a lower quadrant home and distant arm, but the novelty of the LSWR installation was that the signals' normal state with no trains about was in the clear — off — position *(Picture 67)*. After a train had passed and occupied the track circuit in advance of the signals, both arms returned to the on position. They remained so until the train passed the 'clearing point' (or 'overlap') of the next set of signals, after which the home of the first signal cleared while the distant remained on. When the train passed the third signal (and overlap) — two sections ahead — the distant signal of the first set dropped to the off position. And so the sequence continued.

The system worked very well and many of the signals remained in use until 1966. Nevertheless, the idea of signals normally in the off position was not acceptable to the majority of contemporary signal engineers brought up on the closed block system and it was not until after World War 1, with the

spread of colour-light signalling, that the LSWR's rule-breaking principle was adopted as standard for installations of automatic signals.

When the NER chose to install automatic signals on its main line between Alne and Thirsk Green Lane Junction in 1903, the normal position of the semaphores was in the on position. As with the LSWR installation, each automatic signal consisted of a lower quadrant home and distant semaphore on a tubular steel post. American pattern Hall's 'electro-gas' signals were chosen. The power to move the rods to the arms was carbonic acid gas generated in a container at the base of the post, with an electro-magnet to control the valves.

When an approaching train occupied a track circuit two sections in rear of a set of signals, both arms would drop to the off

Below (66):
Sykes electro-mechanical equipment inside St John's B signalbox, SECR. The 36 signal slides can be clearly seen above the mechanical point levers. Immediately below the slides are the Sykes Lock and Block plungers and switch hooks, and above the slides the 'LOCKED' and 'FREE' indications.
Ian Allan Library

position, provided that the two sections in advance of those signals were clear (including an appropriate overlap — the clearing point). If only one section was clear, only the home signal would lower, and if another train was already within the section controlled by the signals, the arms of course remained firmly in the on position. Once the train had passed, both arms returned to the on position.

There were a number of problems that had to be solved before the Board of Trade would give its approval to the NER installation and this was exploited by those with a reactionary viewpoint. An anonymous author writing in the *Railway Magazine* in the summer of 1905 was not at all sympathetic when reporting delays and wrote, 'The sun has risen and set many hundreds of times since the date fixed for the inauguration of this American novelty, but we do not hear that the system is yet in use...which may, or may not, act, as the fit takes it...'

After a number of modifications, Board of Trade approval was secured in June 1905 and the scheme was finally completed in February 1906. But some still remained sceptical, and another *Railway Magazine* report in 1909 yet again cast doubt on the reliability of the track circuits. Despite all these reservations, the signals remained in use until 1933. In 1909 the GCR installed the same design of signals between Whetstone and Ashby Magna but in this case they were arranged as separate stop and distant signals.

Not quite true automatic signals, but just as vital in the development of modern signalling practice, were 'Intermediate Block Signals' (IBSs). Once again the use of such technology had been anticipated by earlier signal engineers, notably Spagnoletti. In the late 1860s he had developed an electrically-operated signal, activated by the passage of a train over a treadle, and commented prophetically that instead of building signalboxes which only operated signals in order to break up long sections, his automatic signals could be used instead.

It was entirely appropriate, therefore, that such signals did eventually come into use on the GWR to divide long sections. They started life as 'advanced section' signals, installed at Basildon on the GWR main line between Goring and Pangbourne in August 1907. As with fully automatic signals, their operation relied on track circuiting. Separate power-operated home and distant signals were provided in advance of the starting signal of the controlling signalbox. The IBSs were in effect the signals of a phantom signalbox; in fact in later years many signalboxes were abolished and replaced by IBSs. The IBSs were controlled by one lever in the signalbox in rear of them. Providing the signalman had received a 'line clear' from the signalman in advance, when this lever was pulled, the IBS home and then distant signals would drop to the off position. As soon as the train passed the signals they returned to danger, and could not be cleared again until the train had passed the clearing point or overlap (usually 440yd) beyond the IBS home signal and another 'line clear' had been sent.

Rationalisation

It was partly due to the introduction of power signalling, and to the reduced demand for mechanical equipment once railway companies had responded to the requirements of the 1889 Act, that led to big changes in the signalling business in the period covered by this chapter.

In 1901 the Pneumatic Electric & General Engineering Co Ltd (later the Consolidated Signal Co Ltd) was formed as an umbrella organisation for Saxby & Farmer; McKenzie & Holland; Evans, O'Donnell; and Pease & Co. Over the next few years the shares of all these individual firms were acquired by the holding company and in 1903 the Railway Signal Co was brought into the fold as well.

In 1907 the McKenzie Holland & Westinghouse Power Signalling Co Ltd was formed, and during World War 1 the individual companies within the Consolidated Signal Co relinquished their separate managements. Eventually in 1920, the Westinghouse Brake Co Ltd absorbed the Consolidated Signal Co to become the Westinghouse Brake & Saxby Signal Co Ltd, concentrating manufacturing at Evans, O'Donnell's 1894 works at Chippenham. In the 1920s and 30s, the firm became one of the major signalling contractors in this country and by 1936 was able to boast in an advertisement in *Modern Transport* that its factory had almost doubled in size.

The 'real' Saxby & Farmer's Kilburn works had closed in 1903 and McKenzie & Holland's in Worcester finally succumbed in 1921. The British Pneumatic Railway Signal Co continued independently, trading as the British Power Railway Signal Co from 1918. The Siemens interest transferred to the Siemens & General Electric Railway Signal Co (SGE) in 1926, and it was joined in the signalling contractors' market by the General Railway Signal Co (GRS), or to give it its correct British title, Metropolitan-Vickers GRS Ltd. Only a few years after the Grouping in 1923, British railway signalling was about to enter a new era of all-electric power signalling.

Left (67):
A gantry of eight pneumatic automatic semaphores on part of the LSWR's line between Woking Junction and Basingstoke. From left to right the signals (home and distants) read: line clear one section ahead; ditto; train just passed and section blocked; at least two sections ahead all clear. The hut beneath the gantry protected the fogman and contained a ground frame connected to Clayton's automatic detonator placers, two of which are clearly visible in the foreground. When the lever was operated, the placer automatically discarded the spent detonator and loaded another from the vertical metal boxes at the rear of the mechanism.
National Railway Museum (329/87)

4 Standard Lights 1918-39

The interwar years were another revolutionary period for railway signalling. At the end of World War 1 the steam locomotive was the main form of traction on Britain's railways. By the beginning of World War 2 nothing had changed. In 1918 oil-lit lower quadrant stop and distant signals, displaying just two aspects and worked from mechanical lever frames, were the standard pieces of equipment in the majority of signalling installations from one end of the country to the other. By 1939, there were thousands of new upper quadrant semaphores in operation, as well as hundreds of colour-light signals capable of displaying a nationally-agreed set of four aspects. Immediately before the outbreak of World War 2, these colour-light signals protected all but five major London termini (St Pancras, Marylebone, Euston, Liverpool Street and Broad Street), as well as a number of provincial centres. They also controlled trains over the 38-mile stretch of main line between Coulsdon and Brighton, the 13½ miles between Waterloo and Hampton Court, and the 44 miles of track between Skelton Bridge (just outside York) and Darlington.

At the end of the 1930s, although there were plans for more main line electrification schemes, locomotive engineers would probably still have claimed that the steam engine was the most cost-effective means of hauling trains and was likely to remain so into the foreseeable future. For the signalling engineer, mechanical lever frames and semaphore signals had had their day. Colour-light signals may still have been in the minority compared to semaphores, but they were undoubtedly the signal of the future. The traditional mechanical signalbox had still not yielded completely to the latest signalling panels with route-setting switches, but it was obvious this would happen eventually, if and when the capital became available. For the signal engineer the future was all-electric (*Picture 68*).

As with the signalling revolution of the 1870s, what occurred between World Wars 1 and 2 was the bringing together of a number of elements which together transformed accepted traditions. Many of these elements were not new but in combination their effect was revolutionary. What happened in the 1920s and 1930s was the transformation of theories into practical installations at various locations around the country.

The Elements of Transformation

The first element, which may not at first seem obvious, was a real increase in wages and consequently labour costs compared with prewar years, due to inflation and the introduction of the 8hr day. Whereas before World War 1 the cost of extra signalmen if extra signalboxes had to be built was only one cost implication, between the wars labour became an expensive commodity. The scarcity of jobs, of course, kept wages relatively low, but equally that scarcity was because railway companies, as with all British industry, could not afford the labour. Throughout this period the contemporary articles, as well as extolling the virtues of the new technology, invariably mention the economies this would bring about, and by economies they meant less people. Immediately before World War 1 there were just over 28,500 signalmen working on Britain's railways. Between 1922 and 1938 that number was reduced by 4,407.

The remaining elements were technological ones. Frames of miniature levers or slides had proved themselves by 1918 and electric motors had improved enough to be an accepted means of operating points and semaphores. Track circuiting came of age between the wars, as did relays and relay interlocking. One element which was conceptual but became of revolutionary practical use as the design of day-time, colour-light signals was perfected, was the formulation of, and then general agreement to use, three basic signal aspects for both semaphore and colour-light signals. Almost as soon as this was agreed, a fourth aspect was added to the suite, which still remains the basis of colour-light signalling to this day.

The real innovation of the 1920s and 1930s, which needed all the above elements to be completely successful, especially track circuits and relay interlocking, was route setting. The idea was not new, having come from France where an installation was shown at the Liege Exhibition in 1905. But its practical implementation in this country put Britain in the forefront of its development and its application is still at the heart of late 20th century computer-driven signalling technology.

The Elements: Points

'Looking back over the past 10 years, one development alone, to my mind, marks this as the most remarkable decade in the history of signalling, and that is the introduction of the low-voltage point machine, coupled with the Ministry of Transport's amended "Requirements", which withdrew the restrictions on the distance at which points could be power-worked from a cabin (signalbox), providing certain necessary safeguards were introduced. Thus at one stroke of the pen the whole theory of signalling altered. This document may well be regarded as the signal engineer's Emancipation Act, for it enables infinite rearrangements tending towards economy and

Below (68):
This photograph has been included to show that although there were revolutionary developments in signalling between the wars, drivers of some of the fastest trains in the country still had to look out for oil-lit pre-Grouping semaphores. Here LNER 'A4' No 4492 *Dominion of New Zealand* pulls the down 'Silver Jubilee' through Harringay in the late 1930s, still protected by ex-GNR somersault signals. *Colling Turner Photos Ltd*

efficiency: economy by the closing of signal cabins which are no longer necessary and efficiency because of the simplification in the working of long-distance points without the need for staffing additional cabins.'

These were the opening remarks of an article published in the March 1929 edition of *Modern Transport* under the title 'Ten Years of Railway Signalling'. The author was the innovative A. F. Bound, Signal Engineer of the Southern Section of the LNER, who had been responsible for the pneumatic signalling installations on the GCR and the all-electric scheme at Cambridge in 1926. In 1929 he moved to the LMS to become that company's Chief Signal & Telegraph Engineer; among his many achievements for his new employers was the Mirfield speed signalling scheme of 1932.

The Elements: Three-Aspects and Colour-Light Signals

The spread of colour-light signalling was probably the most significant achievement of the period. Until then, the semaphore was the unquestioned day-time signal, which was supplemented at night by coloured lights, only because the arm could not be seen. At the opening of the 20th century signal lamps remained alight both day and night, but only a few decades previously, they had only been lit at dusk, and were extinguished again at the break of day.

The first experiment in this country to ascertain the effectiveness of an electric colour-light signal in daylight was carried out by A. E. Tattershall, who was to become one of the most influential signal engineers in the 1920s and 1930s. In 1913, when Signalling & Electrical Assistant to the Engineer of the Metropolitan Railway, he carried out a number of tests and published his results in the *Railway Engineer* for August 1914. World War 1 hindered any further work, but in 1920 the Liverpool Overhead Railway installed the first colour-light signals to control a surface railway in this country. Then in the following year, the report of a committee set up by the Ministry of Transport to look into the use of colour-light signals was published. Among its findings it remarked that such signals:
a) compared favourably in initial cost and maintenance with other signals;
b) gave the same indication day and night;
c) were less likely to give a 'doubtful' indication (ie the angle of semaphore arms could be misinterpreted);
d) were more easy to control and to 'slot' than mechanical signals.

All this interest in colour-light signalling came at a crucial moment in signalling history. Since 1893 part of the Board of Trade Requirements recommended that only two coloured lights be used with semaphore and ground signals — red and green. As a result,

both stop and distant signals displayed either red or green aspects, even though at a stop signal, red was an absolute command to an engine driver to stop, whereas red at a distant signal was only a cautionary indication which a driver passed in anticipation of the next stop signal being at danger. This was obviously not a satisfactory situation because it relied completely on the driver's knowledge of where he was and what type of signal he had encountered showing a red aspect in the dark. It is *the* anachronism of signalling history and its official sanction for over 30 years (1893-1925) is still very difficult to understand, let alone justify.

When British signalling engineers began to look outside this country, particularly to North America, at the end of the 19th century, they realised how useful more than two aspects could be. In the first decades of the 20th century a number of companies had started to modify their distant signals to show a yellow aspect in place of a red one. (By 1920, for example, it was claimed that every distant signal between Paddington and Southall on the GWR had been converted.)

Although there was much debate about this move, it led on to a far more significant interest in the three-position upper quadrant semaphore already common in the USA. When they were adopted in this country, the spectacles were fitted with three coloured glasses, so the signal could display red, yellow or green. The first three-position semaphore was installed in 1914 at Paddington station, but the most influential installations of them were on the GCR's new line at Keadby Bridge, Lincolnshire, opened in May 1916 *(Picture 69)*, on the Ealing & Shepherd's Bush Railway in 1920, and on the SECR side of Victoria station, London, the new signalling there being commissioned in January 1920 *(Picture 70)*.

By then, there was not just debate about semaphores, three aspects and colour-light signals, but about the possible use of single-colour 'position' lights instead of semaphores. In 1918 A. E. Tattershall had installed a three-position 'position' light unit on the Metropolitan Railway and in 1920 W. J. Thorrowgood, the LSWR's Signal & Telegraph Engineer, had another fitted at Waterloo. The signal was based on Pennsylvania Railway practice, there being three lines of lights each with four lamps, the second lamp from the bottom of each line being common to all lines. When the horizontal line of four white lights was illuminated, the signal indicated 'stop'; when the line at 45° above the horizontal was lit, it indicated 'proceed ready to stop at the next signal'; and when the vertical line was illuminated, it indicated 'proceed at full speed'. It was in effect the light equivalent of the three-position upper quadrant semaphore.

All these experiments were closely watched by all signal engineers, both progressive and conservative, and there was much discussion about the possibilities of the new light signals, upper quadrant semaphores and the introduction of a third aspect — yellow — to British railway practice. In 1921 A. E. Tattershall presented a paper on 'Three-

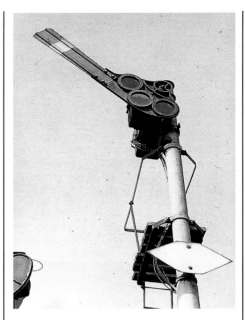

Above (69):
One of the three-position semaphores installed by the GCR at Gunhouse during World War 1. The arm is in the caution position. Photographed in May 1967. *BR(E)*

Position Signalling' to the Institution of Railway Signal Engineers (IRSE), fuelling the arguments and prompting that organisation to set up in March 1922 a Three-Position Signal Committee.

The argument to resist the third aspect and continue to use a red aspect in distant signals was all but lost by then, so the deliberations were between three-position semaphores and colour-light signals. The former had to be power-operated to achieve accurate alignment of the spectacles with the lamp. That made them more expensive to install and maintain than traditional two-position semaphores and in the end more expensive than signals with just lights and fewer moving parts.

A year into the committee's deliberations, the LNER demonstrated its faith in day-time colour-light signals by installing them on the former GCR line between Marylebone and Neasden Junction and over the Wembley Exhibition loop. With the success of these three-aspect day-time colour-light signals and the improvements a third aspect brought to signalling practice, it was almost inevitable that the IRSE committee should champion colour-light signals in preference to three-position semaphores or their 'position' light equivalents, and by the time the committee submitted its report in 1924, it had renamed itself the Three-aspect Signal Committee.

The great advantage of signalling with three aspects in one signal instead of traditional separate stop and distant semaphores was in the improved headways the former provided. In traditional signalling, a distant signal could not be pulled off until all the stop signals it referred to had been cleared. At certain signalboxes more than one stop signal was provided, and in some cases up to four could protect a layout. This allowed a signalman to have a train within the protection of one of the advanced stop signals (the starters), while at the same time being able to accept another train into his block section. The disadvantage of having more than one stop signal was that even though the signalman might be in a position to clear all but one of them, if the most advanced one was at danger, the distant had to remain at caution and consequently the train was checked at the distant, despite the fact that the following signals might then be cleared for its passage as it approached.

With three-position signalling (and this was true of both semaphores and colour-light signals), the logic was always that if a driver encountered a yellow aspect, provided the signalman did not alter his signals after the driver had passed this indication, then the next signal would always be at danger. Likewise, if a driver passed a green aspect, then the following signal in the normal course of events would exhibit either another green or a yellow.

The Elements:
Four-Aspect Signals

Adding a third aspect to the signalling sequence in this way immediately increased line capacity. But once signal engineers understood the possibilities of multiple-aspect signalling (MAS), the potential of using more than three aspects became obvious. As with traditional semaphore signalling, if a driver passed a yellow aspect displayed by a colour-light signal, he would begin to brake in anticipation of a following red aspect just as if he had passed an ordinary distant signal in the on position. Consequently, the distance between three-aspect colour-light signals had to be the same as between semaphore distant and stop signals; in other words, the minimum distance it took the driver of the fastest and worst braked train on the line to bring his train to a stop after seeing a yellow aspect.

Braking distance varied according to the siting of the signal, the length of train, type of motive power and speed. These factors became more significant when the SR began planning the extension of its main line third-rail electrification in the mid-1920s. There was a marked difference between the braking capabilities of the new electric stock and steam-hauled trains and, therefore, line capacity would have been compromised if three-aspect signals had been installed. The solution was a fourth aspect, and this is just what signal engineers Thorrowgood and Challis (both members of the Three-aspect Signal Committee) decided upon.

Between the green and yellow aspect a 'double yellow' was introduced — two yellow lights displayed vertically just under 2ft apart. The use of the double yellow had the effect of providing two alternative braking distances for differently braked trains in rear of a stop aspect. Faster but poorer braked steam-hauled trains could start braking at a double yellow aspect, knowing the next signal they encountered would be a single yellow which they could pass. Better braked electric

units not travelling so fast could effectively ignore the double yellow and begin their braking at a single yellow, in the certainty that they would be able to stop by the time they encountered the next red aspect. Electric trains could, therefore, run safely at their maximum speed past a succession of double yellows.

Double yellows in effect halved the distance between a traditional distant and stop signal and thus increased line capacity. A traditional block section extended from the most advanced stop signal of the signalbox in the rear to the first stop signal of the box in advance. On stretches of line controlled by colour-light signals (particularly automatic ones) the equivalent of the block sections varied depending on the aspect being displayed, because every signal could be both a stop and distant. An important consideration in choosing to use the double yellow aspect between a single yellow and a green, was that if one of the lights failed in a double yellow signal, the aspect became more restrictive (ie a single yellow), not quite fail-safe but 'fail-safer'.

When colour-light signals worked automatically, the train on the track circuits controlled the aspects. Immediately after a train had passed a signal it changed to a red aspect. It continued to show this aspect until the train had passed beyond the clearing point (the overlap) in advance of the next signal, when it then displayed a single yellow. Once the train had passed the next — the third — signal, the first then showed a double yellow, while the second showed a single yellow. When the train had cleared the fourth signal, the first cleared to a green, the second to a double yellow, the third to a single yellow, and the signal that the train had just passed displayed a red. And so the sequence continued.

The Southern Railway installed its first four-aspect colour-light signals between Holborn Viaduct and Elephant & Castle at the beginning of 1926 (Picture 71). Others were erected in the summer of the same year at Cannon Street, Charing Cross and Borough Market Junction and two years later colour-

Above (70):
SR 4-6-0 No 857 Lord Howe departing from Victoria station in the late 1920s. Behind the locomotive is the gantry of three-position semaphores protecting the entrance and exit to the platforms. Real Photographs

light signalling was extended through into London Bridge.

Colour-Light
Signals —
Aspect Conflict

One issue that did not seem to trouble the signal engineers at the time, which considering their other concerns appears somewhat surprising, was the conflict of aspects that arose once the double yellow had become the accepted fourth aspect.

In areas of semaphore signalling, at night a driver might encounter a group of vertically stacked coloured lights for a number of reasons. A stack of reds might indicate a fan of pointwork in a yard. Before the 1920s, two reds vertically aligned on a main running line might be a stop signal with a distant of the signalbox in advance below. If the stop signal was pulled off and the distant remained on, the aspects would be green over red. After the 1920s, the same arrangement would have changed to a red above a yellow with both signals on and green over yellow with the stop signal off and the distant on. Both signals off gave a green over green aspect. In all these cases, the lights would have been at least 3ft (1m) apart. In areas controlled by colour-light signals installed to the SR standard, the only time two coloured lights would appear in a vertical alignment was when double yellows were displayed. Then the lights would be less than 3ft apart.

Although the difference in the space between vertical aspects might have been

considered enough to prevent drivers confusing colour-light and semaphore signals at night, it was still left to their knowledge of where they were as to how they interpreted signals. It can be argued that there was no chance of mistaking a focused electrical beam with the light from an oil lamp. But the GWR was not prepared to accept the anomaly between colour-light signals and semaphore ones, and when it resignalled Paddington, Bristol and Cardiff with colour-light signals in the 1930s, those new signals merely performed like semaphores without arms *(Picture 72)*. Where in semaphore signalling the distant signal of one signalbox was positioned under the stop signal of another signalbox, so at those GWR stations, colour-light signals conformed to exactly the same rules. At these locations, two searchlight signals (for definition see below), one immediately above the other, could display the following 'semaphore' aspects: red over yellow; green over yellow; green over green. Nowhere at Paddington, Cardiff or Bristol would you have been able to see a yellow over a yellow.

On all other companies' lines, colour-lights in the above example would have been electrically slotted. So taking a single four-aspect colour-light signal as an example, when the signalman pulled this off as his home signal, the aspect changed from a red to a yellow. If the signalman in advance then pulled his home signal off, the first signal changed from a yellow to a double yellow. When that signalman cleared his distant

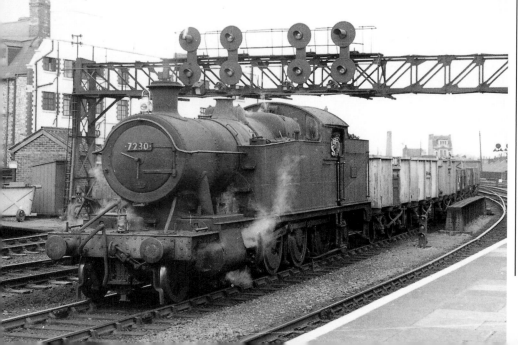

light installations but by the 1930s the arrangement of aspects from top to bottom had been standardised on: yellow, green, yellow, red; the same sequence was adopted by other companies, inherited by British Railways and is still applicable at the time of writing (1997).

ii) Multi-Aspect — Cluster

One of the advantages put forward for colour-light signals was that they could be fixed at a driver's eye level unlike semaphores. Where colour-light signals could not be positioned alongside the track but had to be suspended over it, engineers worried that if they used vertically arranged aspects, the top one would not be easily visible to the driver.

So at Blackfriars and Cannon Street, the SR installed a number of 'cluster' colour-light signals, the four lamps arranged as a cross — the yellow aspects vertical, the red and green either side on a horizontal alignment (*Picture 74*). When the LMS resignalled Manchester Victoria station in 1929 it used the same solution. The fear that drivers would not be able to see what aspect was being displayed also led to the use of a small side light lower down the post in the first SR installations.

By the end of the 1920s these fears had proved unfounded, and further installations of cluster colour-light signals and side lights were discontinued. In fact the beam generated from colour-light signals was so good that it soon became clear that fogmen would no longer be needed at the new signals, another success for economy (*Picture 75*).

iii) Searchlight

Another perceived problem with multi-lens signals was the possibility of strong sunlight shining into the lens to make it appear as though the lamps were illuminated. Hoods were fitted as standard from the early 1920s, but the possibility of 'phantom' or false indications led companies, most notably the LNER and GWR, to use 'searchlight' or 'Hall-type' colour-light signals instead of multi-lens units. In these type of signals, the different aspects were projected through one lens, with a spectacle housing three colour glasses positioned just in front of the bulb. The aspect was altered when the 'spectacle' was moved mechanically in front of the bulb. The disadvantage of the searchlight signal was its inability to show more than three aspects. To achieve the fourth aspect — the double yellow — when this was required, two units were mounted vertically above each other. The bottom unit was capable of displaying all three aspects, while the top unit only displayed a yellow when a double yellow was needed, and at all other times was not illuminated (*Picture 76*).

iv) Mechanical

One of the strangest experiments in the development of the colour-light signal was carried out by the LNER in the early 1930s. A

signal, the first signal aspect changed from a double yellow to a green.

Although the GWR had logic on its side, making sure there was no difference between the aspects displayed by its colour-light and semaphore signals, the progressive use of four-aspect colour-light signals was accepted by all the other railway companies after 1926 (*Picture 73*).

Colour-Light Signals — The Choices

Where possible, colour-light signalling, using two, three and four aspects, was preferred for major resignalling projects by three of the Big Four companies — SR, LNER, and LMS

excepting the GWR —from then on, and in 1932 the *Railway Gazette* commented that '...colour-light signalling may be regarded as accepted practice in this country and well beyond the experimental stage'. But the multi-lens colour-light signals we take for granted today, and which were first used by the SR in 1926, had their rivals between the wars.

i) Multi-Aspect — Vertical

The standard configuration pioneered by the SR was to stack individual aspects above each other in a vertical line, each lamp and lens projecting one colour. When the SR first used four-aspect signals, the indications from the top to the bottom of the units were arranged: green, yellow, red, yellow. The LMS also followed this configuration in its early colour-

Above (74):
A pair of cluster-type colour-light signals ready to be brought into use in the summer of 1926 at Borough Market Junction. One tower and part of the roof of Cannon Street station can just be seen in the background. *Modern Transport*

Left (75):
An SR instruction of 1928. *Author's Collection*

SOUTHERN RAILWAY

§PS 2700

Instruction No. 20a, (1928.)

INSTRUCTIONS TO ALL CONCERNED AS TO

Fog-Signalling Arrangements in the London Bridge Bricklayers' Arms Junction Colour Light Signalling Area.

All concerned to note that Fog-Signalmen will NOT be provided at any of the Colour Light Signals between London Bridge (including the Borough Market Junction Down Starting Signals) and Bricklayers' Arms Junction and the undermentioned entries shewn on Page 20 of Supplement No. 1 to the Eastern Section Time Tables relative to working of Steam and Electric Trains under conditions of Fog, Ice, or Snow (Season 1928—1929) should accordingly be deleted :—

Borough Market Junction Down Through and Local Starting Signals. (D.4, 5, 6, 12 and 14).

London Bridge Up Outer Home Signals (E.262 and 273) for Nos. 1 and 2 Up Lines.

EDWIN C. COX,
Chief Operating Superintendent.

WATERLOO STATION,
31st October, 1928.

(R. 16997)

few miles north of Northallerton, Danby Wiske and Birkby signalboxes were closed in 1932 and automatic colour-light signals erected in their place. As part of the work, mechanical three-aspect colour-light signals, made up of standard upper quadrant semaphore spectacle castings with no arms attached, were installed and controlled from Hunwick, Cowton and Wiske Moor signalboxes. At the latter, there was a home over distant signal arrangement, mechanically slotted in the normal way. But the aspects displayed were not standard semaphore aspects, but colour-light ones. When both spectacles were in the on position, the top (home) one showed a red aspect while the lower light (the distant) was extinguished. When the home signal was pulled off, its light was extinguished and the lower light illuminated to shine through its yellow spectacle glass. When that spectacle was pulled off, the light shone through its green glass. The light source used was Cooke Fog Penetrating electric lamps, designed and made in York *(Picture 77)*.

Mechanical colour-light signals were installed at other locations on the LNER, and at Black Banks, also north of Northallerton, for example, the aspects of the slotted home and distant signals were differently arranged to those at Wiske Moor. At Black Banks, the top light (the home) displayed either a red or yellow, while the lower light was either extinguished or displayed a green *(Picture 78)*.

v) Approach-Lit

The use of mechanical colour-light signals was to reduce the costs of installing the full electrical versions and the LNER was also keen to save money by installing approach-lit colour-lights. Today we take electricity for granted wherever we are in the country. But in the early 1930s there were still many mainly agricultural areas not connected to the new National Grid. In these areas, where batteries had to be used to power colour-light

signals, the LNER wired the signals so that they were only illuminated when a train occupied a track circuit in rear of them. The LMS also installed a number of approach-lit colour-light signals, the first at Hargate brought into use on 17 April 1932. When the approach-lit Intermediate Block Signals (IBSs) were brought into use between Prees and Whitchurch Cambrian Junction in Shropshire, when Prees Camp Sidings signalbox was abolished on 11 August 1935, the down signals lit when the approaching train was 849yd away and those on the up line when the train was 841yd from the signals.

vi) Route and Junction Indicators

In the SR's first colour-light installations, if a driver was to take a low speed route at a junction, usually on the approach to a station, 'theatre' type indicators above the main signal displayed a number or letter. At junctions leading from one running line to another through route, a separate multi-lens colour-light signal head was provided.

The provision of separate colour-light units for junctions was perpetuated in all the 1920s resignalling projects. Signal engineers, however, disagreed over this continuation of semaphore practice, and there were also practical problems such as a red aspect of one unit overwhelming a green of an adjacent unit.

It was A. E. Tattershall of the LNER who finally introduced the junction indication that is still the standard today. The first experiments were carried out during the York-Northallerton resignalling of 1933. The idea was to provide just one colour-light unit, searchlight or multi-lens, and next to this place a fluorescent tube, angled away from the main signal according to which way the route diverged *(Picture 79)*. The tube was very soon abandoned in favour of a row of five small white lights, derived from Tattershall's use of the position light when he

was employed by the Metropolitan Railway *(Picture 80)*. If more than one route had to be signalled, the lines of lights could be arranged at various angles from the vertical to the horizontal and, if necessary, 45° below the horizontal. The LNER and LMS used a row of five white lights, whereas the SR used a row of three.

It was on the York-Northallerton stretch of the LNER that the traditional ground signal in the form of a miniature semaphore or disc gave way to the use of the 'position' ground signal. This too had come from North American practice and was, and is, the only survivor from the whole concept of position signalling with lights. Three lights were used, two arranged horizontally — red and white — to indicate on, and another off-set above, which when illuminated white with its white partner below (the red being extinguished), indicated off. The 45° angle the two white lights created when illuminated was the light equivalent of an upper quadrant arm in the off position. These ground signals are still today's standard pieces of equipment.

Electric Interlocking

Because the interlocking between levers in a mechanical frame was itself mechanical, the levers had to be aligned in a row so that the locking bars between them could be supported and guided as they moved a predetermined and accurate distance to effect the locking. In the first power frames, the interlocking between the miniature levers or slides was also mechanical, so like their full size counterparts, the levers or slides were arranged in a continuous row. As the area one signalbox could control increased with the use of power-operated points and colour-light signals, so the size of the frames increased, as did the complexity of the locking. At London Bridge the new 1928 signalbox was equipped with a frame of 311 miniature levers in one

Left (76):
'B16/2' 4-6-0 No 61435 waiting for the right-away at Northallerton in April 1960, next to a four-aspect colour-light signal made up of two searchlight units. Above the signal is a 'theatre' type route indicator made up of a matrix of small white lights and below, next to the signal's identity number, is a position-light shunting signal. *G. W. Sharpe*

Right (77):
The LNER mechanical colour-light signals at Wiske Moor, photographed in 1932. *Modern Transport*

Far right (78):
The LNER mechanical four-aspect colour-light signals at Black Banks, disguised to look like standard all-electric ones. The traditional mechanical slotting arrangement is clearly visible half-way down the right-hand post. Photographed in December 1934. *Modern Transport*

57

Far left (79):
A rare photograph showing the experimental fluorescent tubes used at Thirsk as junction indicators, fitted over the existing colour-light junction signals to left and right of the main post. Copy of an official LNER photograph.
Fastline Photographic, York (8329)

Left (80):
LNER four-aspect colour-light signal made up of two searchlight units, with what became the standard type of junction indicator to the left.
Real Photographs

Below (81):
The Westinghouse frame of 311 miniature levers at London Bridge. *Topical Press Agency*

Right (82):
Part of the miniature lever frame in North Kent East, the first relay interlocked frame in the country, brought into use on 1 December 1929 as part of the resignalling between London Bridge and New Cross. *R. K. Blencowe (33513)*

row over 64ft long *(Picture 81)*. The frame was massively constructed because it had to be absolutely rigid to maintain the integrity of the complex mechanical interlocking. This, combined with the number of locking bars needed, meant the frame weighed approaching 23 tons. The installation work at London Bridge had been carried out very carefully and the interlocking tested very thoroughly, to make sure no locking bar had become deformed or, more importantly, could become deformed in continuous use. Mechanical interlocking had undoubtedly reached its physical limits, and the frame at London Bridge was the last frame of miniature levers so equipped.

The next development retained the tappet bars and the equivalent of the locks but instead of the locks, being physically connected to each other by locking bars, the latter were replaced by electrical circuits running through relays — relay interlocking *(Picture 82)*. Instead of one lever physically pushing the lock out of the tappet bar of another lever to either lock it or free it to be reversed or pushed back in the frame, the moving of one lever operated a relay which 'picked' the lock of another lever's tappet bar, thus locking or freeing it. This not only dispensed with a lot of ironmongery in the form of locking bars and locks, it also meant that levers or slides no longer had to be arranged in one continuous row.

Only the SR exploited this freedom. The first frame of miniature levers to be divided into separate sections was installed at Brighton in 1932. There the 225-miniature lever frame was split into three sections, with the outer sections angled so the three signalmen could all see the two illuminated diagrams provided. The same tripartite

arrangement followed at Waterloo in 1936 — 309 miniature levers divided into three sections containing 75, 159 and 75 levers each — and finally at Victoria Central in 1939. These signalbox interiors were obviously different from anything that had gone before and had the feel of modern control rooms. The back to back arrangement of the miniature lever frames installed by the LMS at Crewe North at the outbreak of war looked old-fashioned by comparison.

Route Setting

It is surprising that the SR did not take relay interlocking an important stage further. That was left initially to the GWR, whose conservatism inevitably got the better of it at the end of the 1920s, when it ceased further development, leaving the LNER to exploit 'relay route interlocking' using panels of switches, a move which took railway signalling into a new era.

The principle of any interlocking was to ensure that signals and points were cleared in the correct order to set up a path — a route — for a train to travel along. One lever had to be moved for each set of points in the route and only then could the signal lever(s) be operated. Consequently signalmen had to move a number of levers before a route was set.

The next logical step was for that sequence to be semi-automated, so that the operation of one lever should start a chain reaction. If one point moved correctly, provided that conflicting points and signals were properly set, and that it was proved to have responded correctly, then another piece of equipment — point or signal — would move, checked

against conflicting points and signals, to be proved itself before the sequence continued, until all the necessary points had set up the correct route and the signals controlling that route could clear, to allow the train to pass along it. In practice several points could move simultaneously as long as they were non-conflicting.

The first form of 'route setting' in this country was patented in 1918 (No 125028) by Siemens, Ferreira and Insell, based around a frame of miniature levers. L. M. G. Ferreira was employed in the Siemens Brothers signalling department and Robert James Singer Insell was Chief Assistant Signal Engineer of the GWR. The first practical installation of their system was in 1922 at Winchester Cheesehill on the Didcot, Newbury & Southampton Railway.

At Winchester all levers (except the King lever) corresponded to signals, and there were no point levers. For example, if lever No 1 — the up main home signal — was reversed to the first intermediate notch in its travel (the 'check-lock' position), three sets of points were either moved automatically to, or proved to be in, the correct position before the lever could be fully reversed to lower the semaphore to all clear, to allow the train forward to the starting signal, No 2. At the same time any conflicting routes were locked. By pushing the miniature lever back to its second intermediate notch, the semaphore could be placed to danger, but the lever could not be fully replaced until the train had cleared the track circuit protecting the three sets of points. Until another route had to be set up, the points remained in whatever their last position was.

Behind each lever there was a set of vertical lamps indicating red when the signal

was on and green when the signal was off. Between those two lamps were orange and white indications. When the lever was pulled to the first of four intermediate notches and the appropriate points had been moved, the orange lamp illuminated. When the track circuit proved to be clear, the red and orange indications were joined by the white one. This told the signalman the route was correctly set and he could pull the lever to its fully reversed position. This extinguished the three lights and lowered the semaphore, which then lit the green lamp behind the lever.

In the Winchester frame, lever No 9 was designated the King lever. Normally it was kept in an intermediate position in the frame, but when points had to be operated separately in cases of emergency it was pulled to the reverse position, this action freeing slides located just below the levers, which could then be used to work the points. When pushed to the normal position, the King lever could also be used to release the backlock of a signal lever if it had failed to allow that lever to be replaced to normal in the frame. If signalmen had to resort to this action, however, they were strictly instructed to enter details in the Train Register.

The layout at Winchester was very simple, but the advantages put forward for route setting were: firstly, the reduction in time it took to set a route compared to a signalman having to move a number of point and signal levers manually, often spread throughout a traditional mechanical frame, and secondly, the reduction in the number of levers required. The 16 miniature levers at Winchester replaced a mechanical frame of 24 levers, but it was stated at the time that in

Above (83):
Newport East signalbox photographed in the mid-1950s.
P. J. Garland Collection/R. S. Carpenter/ D. J. Powell Collection

Below (84):
Official LNER photograph of Thirsk signalbox taken just before Christmas 1933. *LNER*

fact the route-setting frame did the work of an equivalent mechanical frame with 32 levers.

The success of the Winchester experiment led the GWR to commission an altogether more impressive installation at Newport five years later when resignalling work became necessary there. The work of four mechanical signalboxes was taken over by just two — Newport West and East — with 144 and 96 miniature levers respectively (*Picture 83*).

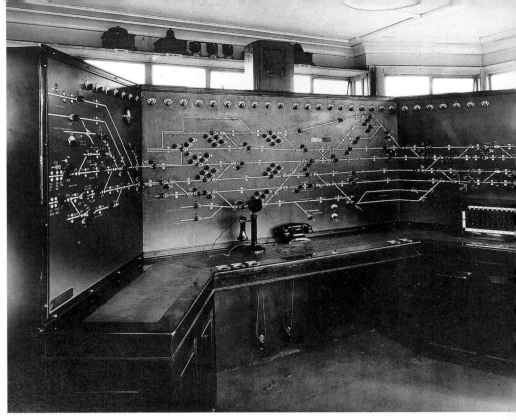

The frames were the same type as installed at Winchester, which apart from the emergency point slides had become the standard Siemens & General Electric (SGE) Railway Signal Co product. Traditional block working was retained and the illuminated diagrams were designed to conform with the earliest ideas for such equipment, that the track circuit lamps should remain alight until a train occupied a track, at which time the lamps were extinguished (the exact opposite of later practice).

The equipment at Winchester was replaced by a standard lever frame in 1933, but the SGE frames at Newport remained in use until 1962. Inexplicably, the GWR installed no other route-setting frames after 1928. Perhaps the company did not trust the technology at layouts more complicated than Newport. The reasons are no longer clear. The miniature lever frames installed at Cardiff East and West in 1934 were simply miniature versions of standard mechanical frames with the tappet locking replaced by relay interlocking, and at Bristol, where route setting would have been a real boon to the signalmen, two massive frames of 368 and 328 pistol-grip slides were commissioned during 1935, each slide operating only one item of trackside equipment. Watching the two signalmen in Bristol East manipulating 368 slides may have been impressive, but their job had been made unnecessarily difficult when the technology of route setting was available.

The company which took up the torch of route setting, developed it, and took railway signalling into another dimension, was the LNER. By the end of the 1920s, electrically-operated points and signals worked from miniature lever frames were acceptable to all but the most reactionary signal engineer. By then the miniature lever no longer had to drive metal tappet bars through locking trays of locking bars and locks, it was merely a switch guiding an electric current through a number of relays which 'tested' the position of points and signals as a locking bar and locks would have done, before allowing another current to operate individual points or signals. There was no reason why the miniature lever could not be replaced by an electrical switch. But despite the progress made in railway signalling until then, it was still a bold move to eliminate the traditional lever or slide, a decidedly masculine working tool, and replace it with switches that resembled those becoming increasingly familiar on new domestic electric cookers. The signal engineer who dared to bring this change about was A. E. Tattershall.

At the beginning of 1933 Tattershall designed a resignalling scheme at Goole swing bridge. The two signalboxes either side of the bridge and the station box were closed. The equipment in Boothferry Road signalbox was modified to operate both colour-light and semaphore signals, but the most important feature of the work was the fitting into the swing bridge cabin of a panel of switches to operate signals and points. It was the first time 'thumb-switches' had been used on a British railway in this way. The signal switches were positioned on the track diagram next to the icon of the signal they controlled, while beneath this the point switches were arranged in a horizontal row as in a mechanical frame layout.

But it was not route setting, and the work at Goole was soon assigned to the list of overlooked signalling developments when in November 1933 the first route-setting panel with thumb-switches was brought into use at Thirsk on the LNER main line between York and Northallerton. As at Goole the switches were arranged geographically on the track diagram, but at Thirsk the operation of one switch was capable of setting up a complete route, involving the moving of points and the activation of colour-light signals *(Pictures 84 & 85)*. The installation at Thirsk introduced the 'panel' to British railway signalling (if we ignore the push-button console installed by the GCR in 1907 at its Wath Concentration Sidings). The panel eventually became the standard for resignalling projects and was superseded only at the end of the 1980s.

After 1933 the LNER was securely in the forefront of signalling developments and the company consolidated its position in 1938 when the route relay interlocking — route-setting — panel was brought into use in the new Hull Paragon signalbox on 23 April. As the track layout was more complex than at Thirsk, the route switches were incorporated into a sloping console beneath the vertical illuminated diagram. This arrangement became the standard for all subsequent Westinghouse 'One Control Switch' (OCS) panels. In front of the switches were descriptions of the routes they operated — 230 routes in total. Switches that controlled main route signals were coloured red, and those controlling subsidiary routes, white. In effect each signal could be operated by turning a number of different switches, depending on which route was required. Black switches immediately below the illuminated diagram were provided for emergency point operation. Detonator placing switches were coloured green and ground frame release switches coloured orange.

Just as war was being declared on Germany in 1939, the second OCS panel, capable of setting up 129 routes, was being brought into use at Northallerton. But by then, route setting had been taken a stage further using North American technology. On 28 February 1937, one and a half miles from Liverpool Central at Brunswick on the Cheshire Lines Committee route, another route-setting panel had been brought into use. The layout it controlled was very limited, but the technology was very new to this country. The panel incorporated thumb-switches placed along the lines of the illuminated diagram corresponding to the position of the signals, and next to certain of these switches were buttons. The route was set up by turning a thumb-switch at the entrance to the route and pressing the button at its exit. This principle of eNtrance and eXit gave the system its name — 'NX' *(Picture 86)*. The LNER showed considerable faith in its potential and announced that it was to equip Liverpool Street, London, and Stratford with large scale NX panels. World War 2 prevented this and it was not until 1949 that the two London stations were resignalled (see next chapter). But the major breakthrough had been made and if the war had not intervened, signalling in this country would have been poised for another revolution.

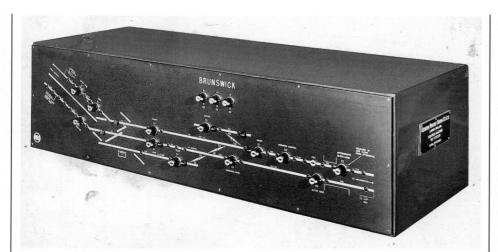

Left (86):
The Brunswick NX panel. *Modern Transport*

Major Resignalling Schemes

Having examined the elements and theories, the following is a résumé of the major interwar resignalling schemes.

Below (87):
Cambridge South a few weeks after it had been commissioned. The tapering corrugated steel semaphore arms are almost identical to the one shown in picture 69. *Sims & Co*

Victoria Station (SECR side)

January 1920
The resignalling of Victoria station with three-position signals places it firmly at the beginning of a new era in railway signalling. As with most of the resignalling schemes between the wars, the aim was to recast the passenger timetable to give a better and more frequent service. The existing signalling would not have allowed this, but three-aspect signalling would, as explained above. The three-position semaphores were semi-automatic, their indications partly dependent on the track circuits and the aspects of the

signals in advance of them. Once a train passed onto the track circuit in advance, the arm returned automatically to danger. The ground signals were three-position discs.

The frame ordered from the American company General Railway Signal Co (GRS) of Rochester, New York, consisted of 200 pistol-grip pull-out slides, the handles pointing upwards and downwards alternately. Interestingly, each crossover road had a separate slide for each point, but the two were connected so that they worked simultaneously. The shanks of the signal slides were painted red and those for points painted black, in line with standard mechanical practice.

Electrical power was obtained from the Westminster Supply Co and was used to power two generators, from which current was either taken directly to the frame or into accumulators. There was also a backup Pelapone gas engine.

Cambridge (LNER)

20 June and 19 September 1925
This scheme was carried out under the supervision of A. F. Bound, newly appointed as the Signal Engineer for the Southern Area of the LNER. Bound had held the equivalent position with the GCR, where he had installed

both pneumatic and all-electric British Power Railway Signal Co (BPRS) equipment. He turned to the same company for the Cambridge all-electric resignalling scheme.

Five mechanical signalboxes were replaced by two new ones containing BPRS frames of draw-slides. The North box had 72 slides and the South had 128 slides *(Pictures 87 & 88)*. The semaphores were all two-position lower quadrants fitted with corrugated steel arms, but colour-light signals were used to control movements over the scissor crossing midway along Cambridge's single platform.

Elephant & Castle-Holborn Viaduct (SR)

21 March 1926
As mentioned elsewhere, this was the stretch of line on which the use of four-aspect colour-light signals was pioneered. The work of seven mechanical signalboxes was transferred to just two — Holborn Viaduct and Blackfriars Junction. The former was the existing overhead mechanical signalbox, re-equipped with a new, 86-miniature lever frame, while a new structure was provided at the latter, fitted with a frame of 120 miniature levers, both frames supplied by Siemens & General Electric (SGE) Railway Signal Co.

Cannon Street & Charing Cross (SR)

27 June 1926
The resignalling work at these two London stations *(Picture 89)* included the erection of four-aspect colour-light signals controlled from miniature lever frames. At Cannon Street the existing overhead signalbox was demolished and a new signalbox was equipped with a frame of 143 miniature levers. At Charing Cross the existing overhead structure survived to be fitted with a new frame of 107 miniature levers. At Metropolitan Junction and Borough Market Junction the signalboxes retained their mechanical lever frames.

Newport (GWR)

29 May 1927 and 24 June 1928.
See pages 60-61 for details of the scheme.

Above right (88):
The interior of Cambridge South with its frame of 128 slides. The tappet locking can just be seen in the glass-fronted cabinets beneath the slides. *Sims & Co*

Right (89):
Charing Cross, showing the semaphores and overhead signalbox brought into use in February 1888 with a frame of 119 levers, and re-equipped 38 years later in 1926.
Historical Model Railway Society Photograph Collection (V3038)

Above (90):
London Bridge station in 1928, showing to the right the 1874 Saxby & Farmer signalbox and behind it the replacement signalbox yet to be commissioned. *Ian Allan, Madgwick Collection*

Left (91):
Borough Market Junction, the top of which is currently preserved at the National Railway Museum. *R. C. Riley*

the modifications was the longest platform in the world (2,194ft) and modern colour-light signalling.

Two new signalboxes and a ground frame (which had all the appearance of a signalbox) were erected to take over the work of six mechanical boxes. All were equipped with Westinghouse K frames, Manchester Victoria West Junction boasting 95 miniature levers *(Pictures 92 & 93)*, Deal Street 99 and Irwell Bridge ground frame 15. Some of these levers controlled two pieces of track-side equipment, depending on whether they were pushed or pulled. In the panel above the levers were lamp indicators capable of displaying all four aspects of the lineside signals; above those, also built into the panel, were the block instruments, the indications given by coloured lights. The majority of the signals were four-aspect and, as mentioned at the beginning of this chapter, many of these were the cluster type *(Picture 94)*.

Mirfield Speed Signalling (LMS)

17 July 1932
During the 1920s and 1930s, there was fierce debate among signal engineers about the merits of 'route' and 'speed' signalling. Until then, all British railway signalling had been

London Bridge (SR)

17 June 1928
The work here was really the completion of the Cannon Street/Charing Cross resignalling. It involved installing better connections between what before the Grouping were two largely independent stations at London Bridge, operated by the SECR and the LBSCR.

This amalgamation allowed four mechanical signalboxes to be abolished and replaced by just one new one, equipped with a Westinghouse K311 miniature lever frame *(Picture 90)*. The displaced London Bridge North signalbox had contained two Saxby & Farmer 'Rocker & Gridiron' frames installed back to back and totalling 280 levers. At the

same time, Borough Market Junction signalbox was re-equipped with a 35-miniature lever frame *(Picture 91)*.

Manchester Victoria (LMS)

30 June 1929
Before the Grouping of 1923, the L&YR's Victoria and the LNWR's Exchange stations in Manchester, although adjacent on a through route, had developed independently. When both companies were absorbed into the LMS there was an opportunity to rearrange the track layout to create a unified station. An attempt was made, but the result was not the best possible solution. What emerged from

Right (92):
Manchester Victoria West Junction photographed shortly after commissioning.
Robert Humm Collection

Centre right (93):
The interior of Manchester Victoria West photographed when new in March 1929. Immediately above the miniature levers, built into the panel, are the block instruments consisting of a traditional tapper, a three-way switch for sending 'line blocked', 'line clear', or 'train on line', and red and green lights for indicating 'line clear' or 'train on line'.
Modern Transport

Bottom right (94):
The western approaches to Manchester Victoria, showing a gantry of cluster-type colour-light signals and Deal Street signalbox to the left. *Modern Transport*

the former, the indications and aspects of the signals, whether colour-light or traditional semaphores, telling the driver whether it was clear for him to proceed and, at junctions, what route was set for him. Traditional signalling did not indicate to the driver how fast he could travel. That was left to his knowledge of the route and its permanent and temporary speed restrictions. In North America the philosophy was different and much of the signalling was designed to give the driver indications of the speed at which he should be travelling.

One of the strongest supporters of the introduction of speed signalling into Britain was A. F. Bound. He also had his own ideas about signal aspects, which he explained in detail in a paper delivered to the IRSE in April 1932. In that year, three years after he moved to the LMS from the LNER, he was able to put his ideas into practice on the 2¾ miles of line between Heaton Lodge Junction and Thornhill LNW Junction at Mirfield (*Picture 95*).

Traditional block working was retained at all the existing signalboxes. Running signals were of the searchlight pattern, two units arranged vertically above each other. All the standard four aspects were indicated, with the

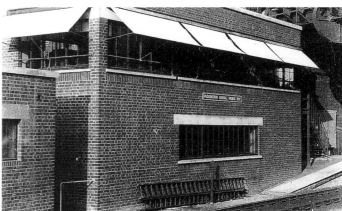

Above (95):
An '8F' 2-8-0 approaching Mirfield No 5 in the 1950s. *Kenneth Field*

Above right (96):
The three-aspect, multi-lens, colour-light platform starting signals at Brighton, just before the commissioning of the new signalling. Just visible on the left is Brighton South, which contained 240 levers in one continuous row installed by Saxby & Farmer in 1882, while on the extreme right is the new replacement signalbox. *Modern Transport*

Right (97):
Paddington Arrival signalbox in its original condition before the fire of 1938. *D. J. Powell Collection*

Below (98):
LNER 'A1' Pacific No 2546 *Donovan* pulling away from Platform 6 at King's Cross on 15 August 1931, past the new but incomplete signalbox on the right and the flat-roofed mechanical ex-GNR King's Cross West box immediately behind the locomotive. *L. Hanson (107)*

Opposite (99):
The 1931 signalbox at King's Cross was a disappointingly conservative structure. At the beginning of World War 2 the elevated locking room was encased with a brick skin which only made it look more conventional. *Modern Transport*

addition between the double yellow and green of a fifth aspect — yellow over green. This indicated 'pass second signal at restricted speed'. At junctions, three searchlight units were stacked vertically. For the main (high speed) route the indications reading from top to bottom were: red/blank/red (danger); yellow/blank/red (caution); yellow/yellow/red (pass next signal on high speed route at restricted speed); yellow/green/red (pass second signal on high speed route at restricted speed); green/blank/red (clear for high speed route). Ignoring the bottom red, these indications were identical with the running signals on plain track. For the medium speed route (in other words, the junction), the indications reading from top to bottom were: red/blank/red (danger); red/blank/yellow (caution); red/yellow/yellow (pass next signal to medium speed route at restricted speed); red/blank/green (clear to medium speed route).

On all posts, beneath the main signals were marker lights which always showed a red aspect, except when a single green aspect was illuminated in the main signal. This practice of equipping marker lights on colour-light signals was standard at the time, no marker light being fitted if the colour-light signal was the last to be encountered by the driver before an area controlled by semaphores.

The Mirfield installation, and Bound's experiments on the Camden-Watford 'DC' and Barking-Upminster lines in 1933, did not convince any other signal engineers to adopt speed signalling and it remained an isolated experiment, surviving until 1970.

Coulsdon-Brighton (SR)

5 June-16 October 1932
This was perhaps the most impressive resignalling scheme of the period, enabling the SR to introduce a fast and frequent passenger service using new electric stock.

The Brighton electrification project emphatically confirmed the company's image as the modern railway and the *Railway Gazette* published a comprehensive supplement in its 22 July 1932 issue, entitled 'The First Main-Line Electrification in England'.

In all, 119 miles of line were track-circuited, all main line running signals were colour-light signals, most of three-aspect, either fully automatic, semi-automatic or controlled from signalboxes. All the latter were pre-Grouping survivors (Redhill and Three Bridges receiving new mechanical frames) except Haywards Heath, which was erected as part of the resignalling scheme with a new 60-lever mechanical frame, and Brighton, which took over the work of six manual signalboxes and was equipped with three frames of miniature levers totalling 225 levers (*Picture 96*). Every signalbox was provided with magazine-type train describers supplied by Siemens & General Electric.

Paddington (GWR)

10 January 1932, 2 July and 13 August 1933
The resignalling between Paddington and Southall with colour-light signals was part of the government's Relief of Unemployment Scheme. Subway Junction was completely remodelled and platforms at Paddington were lengthened. Three new signalboxes were erected as part of the scheme, all equipped with GRS frames with pistol-grip slides. Westbourne Bridge opened on 10 January 1932 with 88 slides; Paddington Departure opened on 2 July 1933 with 96 slides, and Paddington Arrival opened on 13 August the same year with 184 slides.

Block working was retained, standard instruments being used at Westbourne Bridge and panel-mounted ones in the station boxes. All signals were searchlight colour-light signals used, as described above, exactly as though they were semaphores.

Paddington Arrival signalbox was burnt out on 25 November 1938, the replacement

equipment supplied by GRS being put into use on 2 July 1939 (*Picture 97*).

King's Cross (LNER)

19 June and 2/3 October 1932
The very cramped layout at King's Cross was by the 1930s controlled from two low, cramped, flat-roofed, ex-GNR signalboxes, one on the west side with 140 levers, dealing mainly with departures and the suburban platforms, the other on the east side with 100 levers, dealing with arrivals (*Picture 98*). These were replaced by a new but traditionally styled signalbox, built in 1931 and finally equipped with an SGE frame of 232 miniature levers, which was brought into use on 2/3 October 1932 (*Pictures 99 & 100*).

The unchanged layout was signalled with five four-aspect, 17 three-aspect and 40 two-aspect colour-light signals. There were in addition a number of two-aspect ground/shunting signals, 50 disc signals, and 32 illuminated Sykes banner signals prominently displaying an 'S', which instructed drivers to 'proceed in accordance with shunter's instructions'. An unusual feature on the colour-light and banner signals was the provision of white 'back lights' which acted exactly as their equivalent on semaphore signals — the back light illuminated when the signal was in the on position, and extinguished when off.

St Enoch, Glasgow (LMS)

14 May 1933
This scheme was designed by A. F. Bound, one signalbox with a Westinghouse L frame of 203 miniature levers replacing five electro-mechanical boxes. Train describers replaced block working and the illuminated diagram was described as of a type recently introduced as the company's standard. The lines were picked out in colours against a black background, there

being two red lights for each track circuit, illuminated only when occupied by a train.

Cardiff (GWR)

28 May 1933 and 7 January 1934
In 1928 Cardiff Queen Street, on the former Rhymney Railway just east of Cardiff General station, was rebuilt by the GWR and two new mechanical signalboxes — North and South — replaced a number of earlier structures.

Then in 1933/4, Cardiff General, the main station, was itself extensively enlarged and rebuilt. Two new signalboxes were built, both equipped with Westinghouse L frames of miniature levers. Cardiff East, which opened on 28 May 1933, had 154 levers, and Cardiff West, which opened on 7 January 1934, had 339 arranged in one continuous row. Searchlight colour-light signals were installed, giving exactly the same indications as semaphores when installed singly or vertically in pairs as stop over distant signals. Standard absolute block working was retained but the instruments manufactured at Reading by the company were specially designed to fit into the continuous panel above the levers, as at Paddington. Their styling was distinctly Art Deco *(Picture 101)*.

The design of the signalbox structures (similar to those at Paddington) was also striking, with flat roofs and horizontal bands of concrete breaking up the red brick exterior built around a steel frame. As a conscious (and self-conscious) link with the GWR's traditional style of signalbox, the arrangement of glazing bars in the windows was identical to their mechanical predecessors.

York-Darlington Resignalling (LNER)

1933 and 1939
This was achieved in various stages during

Right (103):
The interior of ex-GER Bethnal Green signalbox, photographed just after the line to Hackney Downs had been re-signalled with colour-light signals (the track circuits of this quadruple section show up clearly on the illuminated diagram). The McKenzie & Holland lever frame and the Sykes Lock & Block instruments remained largely unaltered.
Modern Transport

Centre right (104):
Fenchurch Street photographed on 29 August 1911. The semaphores on the bracket were numbered and lettered according to the lines they controlled: F for fast, S for slow, TT for turntable and CS for carriage sidings. The overhead signalbox can just be seen on the right. It contained a frame of 115 levers.
National Railway Museum (GE900)

Bottom right (105):
The 1935 overhead signalbox at Fenchurch Street photographed in May 1959.
Frank Church

1933, with the final work at Northallerton and Darlington completed at the outbreak of World War 2. Five new signalboxes opened during 1933, including Thirsk with its route-setting panel of thumb-switches brought into use on 5 and 19 November that year. A further three boxes were modified existing structures.

All boxes except Thirsk had mechanical lever frames to operate the points, and switches incorporated into the illuminated diagrams to work the new colour-light signals. The latter were three-aspect searchlight types which, although spaced with mathematical precision, did not give an adequate braking distance when the 'Silver Jubilee' train was introduced in 1935. Until the fourth aspect could be installed, a speed restriction of 70mph had to be imposed.

The conversion was not fully completed when Darlington South, with its Westinghouse L frame of 155 miniature levers, was brought into use on 6 May 1939 (*Picture 102*) and Northallerton signalbox with its route-setting panel was commissioned on 3 September 1939.

Gidea Park-Shenfield (LNER)

1 January 1934
The resignalling with four-aspect colour-light searchlight signals along this route was part of the widening of the lines which had progressed as far as Romford by 1931. Just over 11 miles were resignalled, with new signalboxes at Brentwood and Shenfield, containing mechanical frames of 80 and 130 levers respectively, replacing five mechanical ones. Block working was retained but the use of four-aspect signals improved headways and allowed the LNER to introduce a more intensive passenger service.

69

Signals were of the searchlight pattern, some being automatics (each with a telephone for contacting the nearest signalbox) while others were controlled from existing mechanical signalboxes at Hackney Downs, Bethnal Green (*Picture 103*), Seven Sisters, Edmonton Junction and Enfield Town. Seventeen other manual signalboxes were abolished.

Fenchurch Street (LNER)

14 April 1935
Two-, three- and four-aspect colour-light signals were installed between Fenchurch Street, through Stepney East to Gas Factory Junction in 1935. A new overhead signalbox was constructed at the London terminus and equipped with an SGE frame of 140 miniature levers (*Pictures 104 & 105*). In the mechanical signalboxes at Stepney East and Gas Factory Junction, lever locks and circuit controllers were added to the existing frames. Eight other mechanical signalboxes were abolished.

Bristol Temple Meads (GWR)

26 May 1935 and 24 November 1935
The resignalling at Bristol was part of a considerable enlargement of the station. Three

Above (106):
Bristol Temple Meads East photographed on 26 March 1935, exactly two months before it was brought into use. *GWR*

Below (107):
The interior of Bristol Temple Meads East, photographed on 22 November 1960. *BR(W)*

Bethnal Green-Enfield Town (LNER)

22 April 1934, 2 September 1934,
24 February 1935 and 17 November 1935
These dates relate, respectively, to the commissioning of new colour-light signalling between Hackney Downs and Seven Sisters, Seven Sisters and Enfield Town, Hackney Downs to Clapton and Bethnal Green to Hackney Downs.

new signalboxes were built to replace five mechanical ones, the new boxes fitted with General Railway Signal Co Type D frames of pistol-grip slides. Bristol East (opened on 26 May 1935) was fitted with 368 slides (*Pictures 106 & 107*), Bristol West (opened on 24 November 1935) with 328 and Bristol Locomotive Yard with 32.

The frames were of the same design as those fitted in Victoria Eastern in 1919 and Manchester Central (see below). Signals were either searchlights or units with two lenses and, as described above, they merely acted like semaphores without the arms. Power for the Bristol scheme was supplied from a substation at Temple Meads and from the City Corporation, with a diesel-driven standby generator.

Manchester Central (CLC)

23 June 1935
A new elevated concrete and brick signalbox fitted with a GRS frame of 128 pistol-grip slides was erected over the tracks to the southwest of the station. The new signalbox led to the closure of four mechanical boxes with a total of 221 levers (*Pictures 108 & 109*).

Leeds New Station (City) (LNER)

June 1936 and 5 April 1937
This project was planned in 1934 as part of a scheme to improve the layout of what had started life as two separate stations. A brand new signalbox, equipped with a panel of thumb switches, was built at the west end of the station and opened in April 1937 (*Picture 110*), and the existing mechanical signalbox at the east end of the layout (commissioned June 1936) was modified to accommodate a mechanical frame of 25 levers to work the points and a panel of switches to work the colour-light signals, the original frame of 80 levers having been removed (*Pictures 111 & 112*). The panel in the West signalbox was not a route-setting one.

Top right (108):
The new overhead signalbox at Manchester Central station in 1935. In the background to the left is the 105-lever mechanical signalbox of 1881 it replaced.
Reproduction courtesy of the Board of Trustees of the National Museums & Galleries on Merseyside

Centre right (109):
The General Railway Signal Co frame with 128 pistol-grip slides installed in Manchester Central signalbox. On top of the cabinet are the train describers which replaced block working.
Reproduction courtesy of the Board of Trustees of the National Museums & Galleries on Merseyside

Right (110):
The panel inside the new 1937 Leeds West signalbox. *Real Photographs*

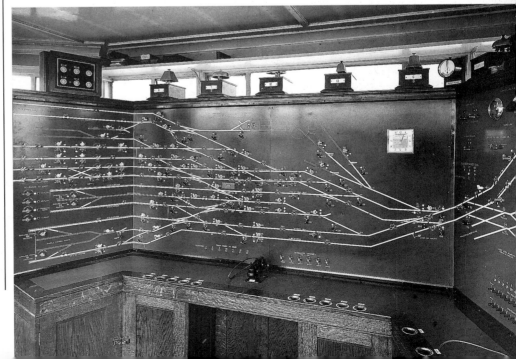

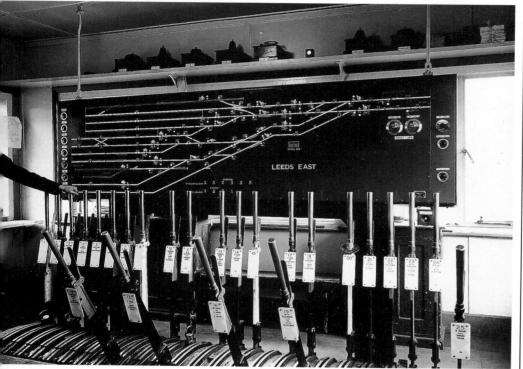

The switches on both panels were arranged geographically on the illuminated diagram, corresponding to the points and signals they operated. The new West signalbox replaced three manual boxes with a total of 250 levers.

Waterloo-Hampton Court (SR)

18 October 1936

The opening of the new signalbox at Waterloo on 18 October 1936 marked the end of the remodelling and resignalling of the main lines out to Hampton Court.

The new box with its 309 miniature levers took over the work of three manual signalboxes at the terminus, including Waterloo A with its two mechanical frames totalling 262 levers *(Pictures 113 & 114)*. New signalboxes were provided at Surbiton and Hampton Court Junction, built to the SR's latest 'Odeon' or 'Glasshouse' style, eight existing boxes were relocked and two — West London Junction and Clapham Junction A (both fitted with electro-pneumatic equipment before the war) — were re-equipped with new miniature lever frames of 59 and 103 levers respectively *(Picture 115)*.

Above (114):
The interior of the 1936 Waterloo signalbox. Next to the track diagrams, the latest 'magazine' type train describers can just be made out; these were beginning to replace Walker's 1874 patent instruments at this time. There were separate receiving and transmitting instruments, both fitted into wooden cases. The receiving instruments had small lights next to a stack of route descriptions arranged in three vertical columns for '1st train', '2nd train' and '3rd train'. The procedure in a signalbox controlling through trains was as follows. When a train approached the signalbox a buzzer sounded and a red light illuminated next to the appropriate description. When the train passed the signalbox, the signalman pressed the button on the transmitting instrument next to the appropriate route, to send the description forward to the next box. After this had been done, the signalman pressed a 'clearance' button to clear the description from his receiving instrument. If there was a following train, the description moved automatically from the '2nd train' column to the '1st train' description slot. The receiving describer could cope with more than three trains, by storing the description until it could be displayed on the describer. There was also a 'receiver full' light which illuminated if there were more trains approaching than the instrument could store. The transmitting instrument only dealt with one train at a time, with a vertical stack of descriptions and lamps. The lamp remained alight after the description had been sent and the train had passed out of the signalman's control, as a reminder to him until the next new description was transmitted. *Modern Transport*

A further 11 former LSWR signalboxes were abolished altogether.

Edinburgh Waverley (LNER)

11 October 1936 and 20 November 1938
The first part of this scheme was completed on 11 October 1936 when the new signalbox and signals at the west end of the station were brought into use. The new signalbox, with a frame of 227 miniature levers supplied by SGE, took over the work of five mechanical boxes with a total of 415 levers. The colour-light signals were of the multi-lens type, those acting as platform starters being fitted with back lights so that a driver of a train standing beyond the signal could look back and see its aspect repeated. Illuminated banner signals were used as calling-on indications above the main aspects, below which were 'warning' signals.

In an advertisement for SGE in *Modern Transport* for November 1936, the company boasted that 'both termini of the famous Flying Scotsman run (are) now signalled with SGE equipment'. The resignalling was completed at the beginning of 1939, when the new East signalbox, containing a frame of 207 miniature levers, was commissioned, train describers replacing block working.

Shenfield-Chelmsford (LNER)

24 October and 12 December 1937
This was one of the LNER schemes which included approach-lit mechanical colour-light signals.

Hull Paragon (LNER)

23 April 1938
The scheme is described on page 61. The signalbox at Hull Paragon is still operational at the time of writing (1997), albeit with a replacement panel.

Shenfield-Southend (LNER)

27 February, 8 May, 22 May and 26 June 1938
This resignalling scheme, and that between Shenfield and Chelmsford completed the previous year, were both continuations of the Gidea Park-Shenfield colour-light installation of 1933 (see page 69). Nine mechanical signalboxes were closed and the frame in

Southend box was reduced from 110 to 81 levers. The new signalling allowed a 3-4min headway between trains travelling on green aspects.

Victoria, London (SR)

16 October 1938, 4 and 25 June 1939
This scheme involved the retention of the 1919 Eastern signalbox with its GRS frame of pistol-grip slides, and the erection of a completely new signalbox (to control the former LBSCR side of the station) built with 14in thick walls designed to withstand air raid damage. It appears that the three-position semaphores and shunting signals had been replaced by colour-light signals and flood-lit disc signals before 1938. In the existing Battersea Park Junction, a new 31-miniature lever frame was commissioned on 16 October 1938. This was followed by the opening of the new Victoria Central signalbox on 4 June 1939 and the resignalling was finished on 25 June that year when the modification work at Victoria Eastern was completed. The new Central signalbox housed a Westinghouse miniature lever frame, with a total of 225 levers divided into three sections.

Crewe (LMS)

25 August and 22 September 1940
By 1939, war with Germany was all but inevitable and all the railway companies had made preparations for the conflict. At Crewe, the LMS felt its North and South signalboxes were vulnerable, so decided to build two new blast-proof replacements and equip them with miniature lever frames to operate colour-light signals. When this was reported in the 18 August 1939 edition of the *Railway Gazette*, no mention was made that Crewe might be a potential enemy target, just that Crewe North and South signalboxes were to be 'rebuilt' to reduce their height.

Other Interwar Resignalling Schemes

Despite this catalogue of achievement, it is important to remember that not all resignalling projects carried out between the wars relied on the latest technology. Renewals of individual manual signalboxes and the replacement of mechanical lever frames continued throughout the period.

In 1928, for example, the GWR commissioned two huge manual signalboxes at Newton Abbot with 206 (Newton Abbot East) and 153 levers (Newton Abbot West) each. Signals were the company's standard lower quadrant semaphores with motor-operated distant signals, and although the layout was fully track circuited, standard block working applied (*Picture 116*). This was by far the largest mechanical installation of the period but other companies were fitting frames with over a hundred levers as well. Two years after the Newton Abbot work, for example, the LNER brought into use a 105-lever mechanical frame on the GN Section of its main line at Newark South to replace two earlier signalboxes. In 1937, when the LNER was equipping its section of the joint station at Leeds with the very latest thumb-switch panels, its joint partner the LMS was building a 100-lever mechanical signalbox at its station at Holyhead (*Picture 117*).

The SR was as progressive as the LNER but took a positive attitude to the installation of mechanical frames. During the 1930s it developed a very modern looking signalbox design which could be equipped with either miniature or full size lever frames. For example, Woking signalbox, opened by the SR in 1937, contained a frame of 131 miniature levers, whereas Horsham and Bognor Regis signalboxes, both built to the same design a year later, had mechanical frames with 90 and 66 levers respectively (*Picture 118*).

The semaphore signal continued to be the most common form of lineside signal between the wars. Having agreed to abandon the use of three-position upper quadrant semaphores, a standard two-position upper quadrant was soon designed and put into production in the 1920s, and all companies except the GWR and CLC used these new arms when existing semaphores had to be replaced (*Pictures 119 & 120*). Gradually throughout the period, the remaining pre-Grouping distant signal arms were repainted yellow, despite the reservations of signal engineers such as A. F. Bound who, while supporting three- and four-aspect signalling, believed that painting arms yellow reduced their visibility.

Whether colour-light signalling, replacement of semaphores, the installation of panels of switches, miniature lever frames or mechanical ones, there is no doubt that considerable resignalling progress would have continued if World War 2 had not halted almost all progress.

Above (118):
The SR's new Bognor Regis signalbox photographed in June 1938. *SR*

Right (119):
The CLC produced its own upper quadrant semaphores between the wars and this photograph, taken in August 1959 at Hunts Crossing, shows two examples.
M. H. Walshaw (6713)

Below (120):
Upper quadrant signals at Connington South on the ex-GNR main line, photographed shortly after they were installed in 1942. The arms of the distant and the shunting signals are the earlier standard pattern of the late 1920s — painted corrugated steel — while the home semaphore arm is of the later enamelled type which was used for most new work after World War 2. *LNER*

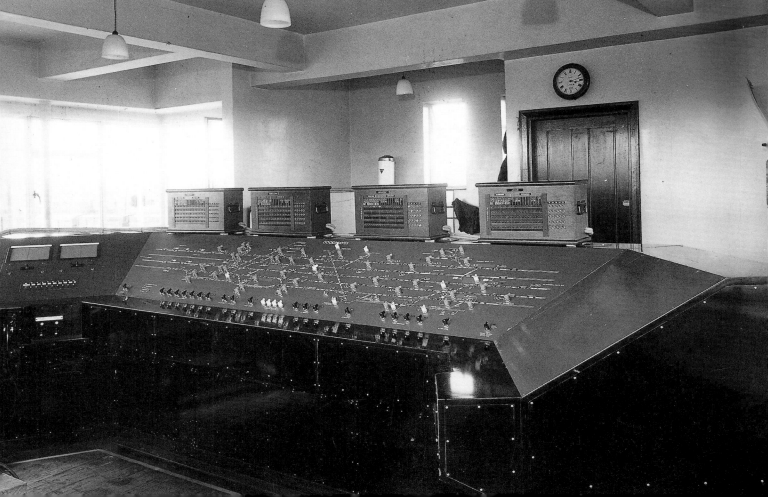

5 Nationalisation and Modernisation to 1966

After the destruction wrought by World War 2 there was a genuine optimism that things would inevitably get better. Change was slow at first, but accelerated during the 1950s and into the next decade. Old buildings were pulled down, towns rebuilt and new roads constructed for an increasing number of privately owned cars. For most people, the standard of living improved, fashions in clothes and popular music all changed, and by the 1960s it was definitely the time to be young and have new ideas.

As all around them changed, it was inevitable that the railways shared the same aspirations of the time and in 1955 the British Transport Commission published its optimistic manifesto for a new era — the *Modernisation & Re-equipment of British Railways.*

The war had seriously delayed the introduction of new signalling technology. The question of mechanical versus electrical and semaphore versus colour-light signals had been resolved before war broke out and the 1930s had shown that the future of signalling was to be fundamentally different from what already existed. Miniature lever frames or panels of switches operating colour-light signals and electrically or electro-pneumatically activated points were the natural choice for new work. Nationalisation did not affect this philosophy and whereas the Modernisation Plan of 1955 led to a complete reversal of British Railways' motive power policy and the far-from-satisfactory introduction of new diesel locomotives, to progressive signal engineers it injected much-needed cash to further their existing aims. In his book *British Railway Signalling* (1969), O. S. Nock recalled how excited he and his colleagues at the Westinghouse Brake & Signal Co were at the substantial investment suddenly directed at resignalling projects. By then, signal engineers had had time to assess the performance of various new equipment installed since the war and had a fairly clear idea of what would be involved to achieve the promised goals of the most prestigious 'modernisation' projects.

The 1955 Plan promised large scale changes after postwar piecemeal improvements. This chapter takes the story of signalling on from descriptions of postwar work, to end with the commissioning of the powerboxes on the West Coast main line in the West Midlands and at Stoke-on-Trent in 1966. The conclusion to the chapter has been chosen deliberately because improving the West Coast main line in order to create a clean, efficient, modern, all-electric railway, epitomises the whole period.

The work also acts as a barometer of that period. It illustrates not only the technological advances made between conception and birth, but also shows how financial realism eventually affected the finished scheme. What had been planned as *the* prestigious resignalling project of the 1950s, became a hybrid scheme to reduce costs at the beginning of the 1960s (it was estimated in 1963 that the resignalling was costing £56,200 per route mile), but finally ended to considerable acclaim with the completion of a string of impressive new powerboxes, far fewer than had been originally envisaged.

It was prestigious projects such as the West Coast electrification that received the most detailed coverage in the contemporary railway press, but it must also be remembered that running in parallel were two other strands of resignalling work, for which there is too little room to make detailed comment here. Firstly there were hybrid schemes involving both new electrical technology and traditional mechanical equipment, and secondly, routine mechanical replacement work which did not form part of any overall scheme. The latter usually involved the replacement of old signalboxes with modern structures which contained new but traditional lever frames, where signalmen continued to control trains using the block system but with the latest design of instruments. Although this distinction is interesting historically, and was significant to those operating signals, points and whole routes, it was of little importance to train drivers. Wherever colour-light signals were used, they displayed a range of standardised aspects, so from a driver's perspective it was immaterial whether those signals were controlled from powerboxes or mechanical signalboxes.

Understanding the technically detailed reports that appeared in the railway press at the time is not easy. As this is not a technical book, this chapter perhaps does not do full justice to a period of considerable electrical engineering achievement. The brief paragraphs below might help the reader make sense of what follows.

Colour-Light Signals

After the war multi-aspect colour-light signals were the accepted visual lineside signal, but there was still the choice of either the single lens searchlight type or those with separate lenses for each aspect. The Eastern Region clung to the use of the searchlight signal longer than any other region, but generally speaking by the 1960s the multi-lens type had become the only choice for running signals. (NB: searchlight signals were installed at most platforms when Birmingham New Street station was rebuilt in the 1960s.)

Signalbox Equipment

In the 1940s and into the 1950s the Southern Region was still fitting miniature lever frames into new signalboxes. At the same time, the Eastern and North Eastern Regions were installing 'one control switch' (OCS) route-setting panels. Elsewhere during the same period, full size mechanical frames were still a viable alternative in resignalling schemes. By the early 1960s the entrance-exit (NX) route-setting panel had become the standard for all major resignalling schemes on all regions. When the OCS panel at Manchester Victoria East was commissioned in 1962, it was already being described as 'dated'.

Relays

Whether mechanical or panel installations, until the beginning of the 1960s, electro-magnetic relays were the norm for all track circuiting. As the area of control of individual signalboxes (powerboxes) increased, so the number of relays required increased, leading to ever larger buildings to house them. The first experiments with solid-state (transistors) in place of relays were carried out on the Western Region at Henley-on-Thames during the summer of 1961. By 1966, miniaturisation was helping to prevent relay rooms from becoming unwieldy, but electronic interlocking was still an area for further development.

Satellite Interlocking

The amount of cabling that would have been needed to connect lineside equipment up to 20 miles away from powerboxes led to the use of satellite interlocking rooms, which were in effect unmanned and semi-automatic signalboxes controlled from parent powerboxes. Satellite interlockings were not eliminated until the end of the 1960s, a development discussed in the following chapter.

Above left (121):
The interior of the new Liverpool Street signalbox, photographed on 2 February 1950. *BR(E)*

Left (122):
The interior of the new Goodmayes signalbox, photographed on 7 September 1949. The four instruments on top of the panel are the train describers. *BR(E)*

Above (123):
The south end of York station, showing the NER semaphores controlled from Locomotive Yard signalbox. Although this photograph was taken by the official LNER photographer at the end of the 1930s, the scene remained largely unaltered until the resignalling of 1951. *BR(NE)*

Below (124):
The same location shortly after the 1951 resignalling, with 'A4' No 60029 *Woodcock* passing through York station with the 'Capitals Limited'. *Real Photographs*

Postwar and Pre-1955 Modernisation Projects

Liverpool Street Resignalling

The scheme to electrify the suburban lines out of Liverpool Street to Shenfield, and the upgrading of the signalling, was planned by the LNER but interrupted by the war. Work began again in 1947 when the track layout at Liverpool Street station was considerably altered, the *Railway Magazine* for July/August 1949 describing the work as '...one of the greatest feats of railway engineering in this country in the last 25 years'.

Colour-light signalling controlled from nine new signalboxes and three existing mechanical ones was finally completed in 1949. Route-setting panels supplied by Siemens and General Electric (SGE) were fitted in the new boxes at Bethnal Green and Liverpool Street (*Picture 121*). At the latter the panel was divided into three sections — 'electric lines', 'main' and 'suburban' — each with its own signalman controlling the lines as far as Bethnal Green including East London Junction, aided by two booking lads and a traffic regulator. On the panels the route switches were arranged geographically on the track diagram. The switches had up to eight route designations marked around the circumferences. This 'selector' switch was rotated until the required destination description lined up with the track. In the centre of the switch was another, which was rotated to lock the selection and initiate the routing.

Goodmayes powerbox was equipped with a Westinghouse 'one control switch' (OCS) panel (*Picture 122*), and in the new Stratford powerbox a General Railway Signal Co (GRS) NX panel was fitted. At Forest Gate Junction, Ilford and Ilford Carriage Shed signalboxes mechanical lever frames operated the points, whilst switches incorporated into a panel operated the signals. Thirty-three mechanical signalboxes were closed as part of the scheme. The first tests of the new electric stock began on 23 March 1949 and the regular passenger service started in the autumn of that year.

York Resignalling

Another ex-LNER scheme completed after the war was the resignalling of York station. The project, announced in July 1937 and delayed by the war, was completed very much as originally planned. Eight mechanical signalboxes with a total of 867 levers were closed, including Locomotive Yard, the largest manual box ever built in this country (*Pictures 123 & 124*). Chaloners Whin and South Points boxes closed on 18 April 1951, followed on 20/21 May by Platform, Waterworks, Leeman Road, Clifton and Locomotive Yard signalboxes, the latter demolished a week later. The new OCS route relay interlocking panel, supplied by the Westinghouse Brake & Signal Co, was commissioned on 27 May 1951. It was staffed by four signalmen per shift with a traffic regulator, part of a team of just 27 people compared with the 70 signalmen employed to man the old signalboxes.

The new panel controlled 33¼ miles of track in and around York including the 16 platforms in the station. There were 79 new three- or four-aspect colour-light signals, 65 of which were fitted with subsidiary signals and 43 with route indicators ('feathers' or lines of small white lights to indicate diverging high-speed routes, 'theatre' type for low-speed ones). Around the station there were 157 sets of points controlled by 277 point machines. Ground signals were of the type soon to become standard for all British

Railways resignalling projects — the 'position light' as used by the LNER before the war.

On the operating floor of the new signalbox, the route switches were at waist height on the console, with switches for individual points and signals above them. Above the console was the illuminated diagram, surmounted by the train describers indicating both class and description of train and the signals they were approaching. The description moved on automatically as the train progressed along its route. A total of 827 routes could be set on the panel, the contemporary *Trains Illustrated* article boasting that 12 route switches and five signals did the job of the former 80-lever mechanical signalbox at Chaloners Whin Junction (*Picture 125*).

When a route was set up, the appropriate tracks on the diagram were illuminated with a string of white lights. This took about 4½ sec, during which time points were moved and detected, signal aspects changed and proved, etc. The longest setting sequence took nine seconds, that being for the route from the down Leeds south of the station to the up main north of the station, involving the moving of 21 pairs of points, their detection, and the locking of 130 conflicting routes.

When the 'train ready to start' plunger was pressed on the platform, the lamp on the diagram in the signalbox would remain alight until the main signal had been cleared. To provide the illuminated indications, the diagram incorporated 5,416 miniature light bulbs. To achieve the necessary interlocking,

Above (125):
The impressive OCS panel at York. *BR(NE)*

there were over 1,000 interlocking relays with nearly 2,000 others for track circuiting, etc. The York resignalling was a very impressive piece of work which, if it had not been for the war, could have been operational during the 1940s. It was some years before this installation was bettered.

Newcastle and Potters Bar Resignalling

The Eastern and North Eastern Regions of British Railways undoubtedly led the way with resignalling projects after the war, building on the pioneering work of the LNER signal engineers. After the success of York, the North Eastern Region secured authorisation in 1953 for a new powerbox at Newcastle to replace the NER electro-pneumatic equipment there. The work took some time to complete as there were conflicting ideas for siting the signalbox. In the end, the new panel was commissioned on 12 April 1959, its area of operation extended a year later to control a further 10½ miles to the east of the city.

On the Eastern Region, quadrupling the East Coast main line between Hadley Wood and Potters Bar gave the signal engineers the

opportunity to control the improved stretch of line from a panel in a new signalbox at Potters Bar. The first stage, which included the rebuilding of the station there, was completed by the end of 1955. Sixteen new multi-aspect signals and 15 ground signals of the position light type used at York were installed.

The new signalbox contained a Metropolitan-Vickers route-setting relay interlocking panel, with switches grouped so they could be worked by one seated signalman (*Pictures 126 & 127*). An illuminated diagram was positioned above the console, which incorporated a smaller diagram with the switches positioned geographically upon it. Above this were individual point switches arranged like a traditional lever frame. These had three positions: central for not in use, with normal and reverse to left and right for use in emergencies. While the points were moved a red light flashed; once the point was correctly moved and proved, a continuous white light showed. Block working was retained, but the instruments, or rather the parts of the instrument (ie tapper, commutator and indicator) were incorporated into the console. When a block bell sounded, it was supplemented by a light indication.

Southern Region's Resignalling of London-Brighton Line (1950-55)

The Southern Region, like the Eastern and North Eastern Regions, continued the innovative work of its predecessor and applied itself to completing the resignalling of the SR's Brighton main line (*Picture 128*). The aim was to abolish the pocket of semaphore signalling from Battersea Park and Bricklayers Arms to Coulsdon, removing the remaining sections of Sykes Lock and Block working and replacing it with continuous track circuiting and colour-light signals. Technologically the whole scheme, costing

approximately £2 million, was not as advanced as those carried out on ex-LNER lines. Panels of switches were not used to operate points and signals, and the 11 new signalboxes contained a total of 841 miniature levers, replacing 32 manual boxes with a total of 1,515 full size levers.

The work was split into four phases, the initial section between Bricklayers Arms and Norwood Junction being completed in October 1950. Phase two was completed in October 1952, when on the 5th of that month semaphores were abolished between Streatham Common and Selhurst, followed on the 12th by those between Battersea Park and Streatham Common. As part of this phase, new signalboxes were opened at Clapham Junction, Balham and Streatham Junction, with a total of 225 miniature levers replacing 11 mechanical signalboxes. The 14¾ miles between Battersea Park and Selhurst was then controlled by 125 multi-aspect colour-lights allowing a headway of 2½ min between stopping trains.

Phase Three was finished two years later, when on 21 March 1954 colour-light signals were brought into use between Norwood Junction and Selhurst and East Croydon. To achieve the final changeover once all the stage work had been finished, 600 men were employed during a 6½ hr possession on the night of 20-21 March 1954.

A new signalbox at Norwood Junction (107 levers) replaced two LBSCR signalboxes with 155 levers, and at Gloucester Road Junction (131 levers), a new structure replaced four mechanical boxes with a total of 235 levers. The new Gloucester Road Junction *(Picture 129)* was a three-storey structure to accommodate the necessary relays and, as stated in the contemporary *Trains Illustrated* article, to provide a good view for the signalman despite the use of illuminated diagrams and magazine-type train describers.

The fourth and final stage of resignalling between Coulsdon North and East Croydon was brought into use on 8 May 1955, the ceremonial last connection being made by C. P. Hopkins, General Manager of the Southern Region, at 7am. The changeover was achieved in a 7½ hr possession with nearly 500 men: 120 semaphore arms were removed *(Picture 130)* and 100 points disconnected and reconnected to the new signalboxes.

The new signalbox at East Croydon with 103 levers had been built during stage three and was already in use as a relay room. It replaced the old North and South boxes, each with 84 levers *(Picture 131)*. The new South Croydon signalbox with 31 levers replaced the station box with 32 levers and the junction box with 55 levers. At Purley, the new 71-lever

signalbox also replaced two boxes, north and south with 52 and 54 levers respectively, while Purley Oaks signalbox with 56 levers, between South Croydon and Purley, was abolished.

Euston Resignalling

In comparison with what the Southern and North Eastern Regions achieved in the early 1950s, resignalling on the London Midland Region in this postwar period was not as technologically advanced nor as extensive.

Liverpool Lime Street was resignalled in 1948, but the Region's only other notable scheme before 1955 was completed on 5 October 1952 at Euston station, when a new signalbox was brought into use, replacing three mechanical ones. The largest was Euston No 2, originally opened on 27 April 1891 with two frames arranged back to back

with a total of 144 levers, replaced in March 1906 by two new ones opposite each other so that the signalmen worked back to back *(Picture 132)*. The work was part of general but modest station improvements which included the lengthening of Platforms 1, 2, 3, 6, 7 and 15.

The equipment chosen to control the new colour-light signals and points was a 227-miniature lever Westinghouse frame that had originally been ordered by the LMS in 1939 for one of two powerboxes at Preston *(Picture 133)*. The work at Preston did not proceed and the two frames were put into store during the war. It is interesting to note that when the signalbox opened, it was already considered by some commentators to be old-fashioned, and certainly the miniature lever frame had a comparatively short life, being replaced in September 1965 by a new NX panel controlling a greater route mileage.

Above (131):
The ex-LBSCR mechanical signalbox at the south end of East Croydon station, with the new cantilever concrete posts and colour-light signals in place and ready for use. Photograph taken in May 1955. *BR(S)*

Below (132):
Euston No 2 signalbox photographed in September 1952, a few weeks before it was abolished. *D. J. Powell Collection*

The frame was operated by three signalmen, with a traffic controller in charge of operations and in touch by telephone and teleprinter with the station and yards. Sixty-one levers controlled 94 electro-pneumatic point machines. Behind the levers were lights to indicate the position of points ('N' normal, 'R' reversed) and signals, up to four indications if the signal was four-aspect. Certain levers were grouped next to route indication lights so that complete routes could be set up quickly.

There were 126 controlled signals, including 32 multi-aspect, 26 subsidiary (with illuminated 'C' for 'calling-on' purposes), and 21 yellow aspect signals for movements to non-track-circuited sidings. Theatre type route indicators were installed throughout. All signal aspects returned to danger automatically once the last wheel of a train had cleared the appropriate track circuit — thus banking engine drivers never had to pass signals at red. Ground signals on the arrival side also returned to danger as the train progressed along its route, while others had to be put back to danger by replacing the lever to its normal position in the frame.

The London Midland Region attempted nothing else like this, or anything more modern until after 1955.

Modernisation Projects

When the British Transport Commission's report on the *Modernisation and Re-equipment of British Railways* was published at the beginning of 1955, among its many wide-ranging promises was the injection of £210 million into signalling and telecommunications improvements, a huge amount for its time. The phasing out of steam traction and the electrification of main lines was another commitment, and the following year it was revealed that apart from on the Southern Region, all future electrification would be at 25kV 50Hz.

Other technical details emerged later, either from official sources, from those inside and outside of the industry, or from reports of actual resignalling projects. For example, in its 1957 Bill submitted to Parliament, the

Above (133):
The Westinghouse miniature lever frame in the 1952 Euston signalbox, photographed shortly before it was commissioned. *BR(LM)*

British Transport Commission mentioned that the third line which it was seeking permission to add to the Southern Region's route between Headcorn and Ashford, would be used for bi-directional running, the first definite proposal in this country for this method of working other than at stations. At the time it was referred to by the French railway term, 'banalisation'. By the 1980s, it was common for lines to be signalled for bi-directional running, enabling a significant reduction of track.

As well as fundamentally new ideas, the modernisation plan also prompted influential engineers such as T. S. Lascelles (President of the Institution of Railway Signal Engineers in 1952 and author of many papers presented to that organisation from 1922 onwards) to announce what he believed were the aims for the upgrading of existing signalling. His views were outlined in a *Trains Illustrated* article for January 1957 and they give us an impression of what had yet to be achieved on lines not benefiting from multi-aspect resignalling controlled from state-of-the-art powerboxes. Track circuiting and colour-light signalling were to be extended and where this was not economical, semaphore distants were to be replaced by colour-light distants to eliminate fogmen. There was to be an increasing use of colour-light Intermediate Block Signals. Electrical controls on block instruments to provide lock & block standards

were to be encouraged, and Lascelles still felt it necessary to remark that Victorian one-wire block instruments had to be replaced. All these were very modest aims compared with what was soon to be achieved on the West Coast main line.

As explained above, the period 1955-66 has been chosen deliberately to encompass the work of modernising the West Coast main line. The period, however, is not an unbroken story of achievement and only three and a half years after publication of the 1955 Modernisation Plan, a White Paper appeared in July 1959 refining its aims. The paper was meant to be optimistic, talking about a speeding up of change, but the underlying impression was pessimistic, indicating a certain loss of faith in modernisation. It was stated that 3,000 miles of track were to be provided with colour-light signals between 1959 and 1963, compared with only 250 track miles converted since 1955. Much of this total was to be achieved with the electrification of the West Coast main line, but it was stated that this and other electrification schemes were suffering through a lack of signalling technicians and by the limited capacity of British signalling contractors.

More rationalisation than originally envisaged was to be considered and resignalling *per se* was no longer to be taken for granted. This certainly made the extensive improvements then taking place on the Kent Coast main line, for example, look both excessive and expensive. Fortunately, 1959 proved a turning point for more positive reasons, and by the early 1960s genuine economies were being achieved as the

technology improved. The route miles controlled from single powerboxes increased noticeably, and the equipment for new projects was becoming more predictable and standardised.

Scottish Region

The effects of modernisation were evident from one end of the country to the other, so it is not inappropriate to begin the survey in Scotland. It is also a useful introduction to the period 1955-66, because work in the Scottish Region demonstrates that new technology was not considered the only means of modernisation; hybrid schemes incorporating traditional mechanical equipment were installed well into the 1960s.

At the end of 1956, the 6¾ miles of Glasgow Low Level lines between Partick and Strathclyde Junction were equipped with colour-light signals. Continuous track circuiting throughout replaced Tyer's lock and block working with treadles, although standard block working was retained (between Partick & Stobcross, and Bridgeton Cross & Strathclyde and Parkhead) with the addition of train describers. Signalboxes at Dalmarnock, Glasgow Green, Glasgow Central Low Level, Anderston Cross and Partick Central No 2 were abolished. Stobcross Junction and Bridgeton Cross Junction signalboxes were retained but re-equipped with control panels above their lever frames. These panels with illuminated diagrams had switches positioned geographically to control signals, while the points continued to be operated from the lever frames.

Left (134):
The NX panel in Hyndland powerbox, photographed when new in 1960. BR(Sc)

Right (135):
D6114 arriving at Perth with the 09.15 Glasgow-Dundee train on 3 June 1966. The new powerbox was a sympathetic addition to the railway scene. C. W. R. Bowman

installation. In the spring of 1958 plans to resignal Perth were announced, the contract being awarded to General Electric Railway Signal Co. The new powerbox, which opened in 1962, was constructed just south of the station *(Picture 135)*, its area of control extending from Hilton Junction, two miles to the south, through the station and the new marshalling yard to the north, to a new 'fringe' signalbox at Stanley Junction eight miles from Perth. Thirteen manual signalboxes were abolished. The new NX panel was capable of setting 470 routes.

North Eastern & Eastern Regions

By the time the Newcastle signalbox opened in 1959, new powerboxes with more up-to-date equipment were being planned for Gateshead, Heaton, Benton and Pelaw, the latter opening on 2 October 1960 *(Picture 136)*. Further up the northeast coast, a new powerbox at Tweedmouth, fitted with a Westinghouse panel, was brought into operation at the end of the following year, leading to the abolition of mechanical signalboxes at Marshall Meadows, Berwick, Tweedmouth North and South. An emergency panel was installed at Berwick.

In the spring of 1962 the first signalbox on the North Eastern Region to be fitted with an NX panel opened at Belford on the East Coast main line, 14 miles south of Tweedmouth. An unusual feature here was the retention of timber crossing gates but fitted with wheeled electric motors. AWS (see Chapter 9), colour-light signalling and continuous track circuiting then extended between Alnmouth and Burnmouth.

Back in the Newcastle area, Gateshead powerbox was commissioned at the close of 1962 (9 December) with the Region's second NX panel supplied by Westinghouse and capable of setting up 232 routes. Signalboxes were abolished at Bensham Curve, King Edward Bridge *(Pictures 137 & 138)*, Greensfield, High Street and Park Lane, all but Bensham Curve with miniature lever frames installed as part of the NER power resignalling scheme. Two years later powerboxes were opened at Benton to the north of Newcastle, and Heaton to the northeast, on 1 March and 6 September 1964 respectively.

On the Eastern Region developments once again focused on former Great Eastern Railway lines. Electrification of the line between Liverpool Street, Chingford, Enfield Town, Hertford East and Bishop's Stortford was officially inaugurated on 16 November

In November 1956 the region was a little more adventurous when it brought into use a route interlocking (OCS) panel in a new signalbox at Cowlairs. The area controlled was only 6½ route miles but the panel boasted 216 route switches, controlling 52 electro-pneumatically-operated points and 40 multi-aspect colour-light signals of two-, three- and four-aspects. Mechanical signalboxes closed at Cowlairs Station, Cowlairs Central, Springburn, Cowlairs West, Cowlairs North, Cowlairs East, Bishopbriggs and Cadder West.

But the region was obviously still unconvinced of either what new technology could do or whether it was economically sound to abandon mechanical signalling altogether. At the beginning of 1957, two new signalboxes, Dumfries Station and Dumfries South, were brought into operation, controlling the ex-Glasgow & South Western Railway stretch of line between Glasgow and Gretna Junction, Carlisle (ie *not* the West Coast main line), with multi-aspect colour-light signals. In the Station box a new panel controlled all signals and points except those points around the signalbox, which were controlled from a 28-lever mechanical frame. The position of both mechanical and electrically-operated points were displayed on the panel. Block working was retained, with the indications given by lights in the panel — white for normal (line blocked), red for train on line, and green for line clear. In the South box both signals and points were operated from a mechanical frame.

Finally at the very end of the 1950s, the Scottish Region seemed to display a more wholehearted commitment to new technology and demonstrated the operational benefits that could be achieved when it resignalled Glasgow Central station. On nine successive Sundays from 8 March 1959, the station was closed to enable the resignalling and track layout changes to take place. As part of the scheme, the late Victorian bridge across the Clyde was removed and six new bi-directionally controlled lines laid across the 1906 bridge. At the time this rationalisation and the avoidance of having to replace the

older of the two bridges was attributed solely to modern signalling which allowed bi-directional running, but in reality this could probably have been achieved by more traditional methods.

On 2 January 1961 the electro-pneumatic powerframe in Glasgow Central was decommissioned and the new Westinghouse OCS panel brought into use. It was divided into four sections, each under the control of one signalman. The entrance buttons were paired with rotary switches which, after depressing the button, the signalman turned until a route became available, indicated by the illumination of a row of rectangular lights on the track diagram. Depending on the direction of the train movement desired, the lights displayed were either white for departures or yellow for arrivals. Above the panel was the illuminated diagram and above that a simplified diagram for the display of the train descriptions, non-standard ones unique to the Scottish Region. The traffic regulator and two telephone operators were positioned behind and above the signalmen to get a clear view of the diagram.

The Scottish Region's next piece of modernisation unfortunately proved a public relations disaster. On 5 November 1960 the new electric suburban passenger service between Glasgow and Helensburgh Central was inaugurated to much acclaim but then abruptly stopped just over a month later on 19 December due to various safety problems. The resignalling in connection with this project was not at fault, but it was a disappointingly hybrid scheme of conservative proportions when compared with the work at Glasgow Central. Two new powerboxes were built at Hyndland and Dumbarton, the former with the latest type of signalling panel — an entrance-exit (NX) panel of rotary switches and automatic train describers *(Picture 134)*. But 25 existing mechanical signalboxes with their lever frames were retained, new panels being fitted to control just the colour light signals.

It was not until the early 1960s that a resignalling project in Scotland displayed all the attributes expected of a truly modern

1960. The signalling was a disconcerting mixture of old and new technology. The existing track circuiting and colour-light signalling out of Liverpool Street to Enfield Town and to Chingford was retained but rewired to immunise it from the new AC traction supply. Eleven mechanical signalboxes were retained, the lever frames continuing to operate the points with the addition of new panels to operate the signals. A new signalbox was built at Ware next to the station level crossing, which received four new lifting barriers controlled from the box. This new signalbox was also fitted with a mechanical frame of 25 levers controlling both colour-light signals and points.

New powerboxes with relay interlocking panels were commissioned at Broxbourne in January 1960, with others at Hackney Downs *(Picture 139)* and Harlow, opening on 28 May and 24 July 1960 respectively. The panels at Hackney Downs, Broxbourne and Harlow were of the latest push-button NX type, the first of the Eastern Region's new design and what became the British Railway's standard design. The entrance button for a forward section also acted as the exit button for the rear section. After being depressed by the signalman, the entrance button flashed until the exit button had been pressed and the route proved. Then the button showed a steady indication while the track between the two buttons illuminated with a series of white rectangular lights and the signal on the diagram changed from red to green. The white lights changed to magenta (red) when a

train occupied that section. To reset the route, the button had to be pulled before being depressed again.

On the other main line route out of Liverpool Street, as part of the introduction of through electric trains from the capital to Clacton and Walton-on-the-Naze, a new powerbox was commissioned at Colchester during the summer of 1962 *(Picture 140)*. As with all Eastern Region schemes at this time,

it too was equipped with an NX route-setting panel, this one supplied by SGE Signals.

On the former London, Tilbury & Southend Railway, which had passed from LMS ownership into Eastern Region hands, another hybrid scheme was completed in the autumn of 1961. Colour-light signalling had been installed by the LNER between Fenchurch Street and Gas Factory Junction in 1935. In Fenchurch Street signalbox the frame

Left (137):
King Edward Bridge signalbox photographed by the official BR(NE) photographer on 6 October 1961, a few months before it was closed. *Fastline Photographic, York*

Below (138):
The interior of King Edward Bridge signalbox photographed on the same day. At the left-hand end of the block shelf are a number of traditional single-needle block instruments and single-stroke bells communicating with Bensham Curve and Greensfield signalboxes, while on the right in front of the signalmen are the train describers to the 1959 powerbox at Newcastle. *Fastline Photographic, York*

Above right (139):
The new powerbox at Hackney Downs with one of the mechanical signalboxes it replaced on the left, photographed on 15 July 1960. Notice the large overhanging roof on the new structure to prevent direct sunlight penetrating the windows of the operating floor. *BR(E)*

Centre right (140):
Colchester powerbox photographed on 14 March 1962. *BR(E)*

Bottom right (141):
The powerbox at Barking photographed in October 1959, two years before it was brought into use. *BR(E)*

of miniature levers was retained in the new scheme and supplemented with a new NX panel to control Stepney East and Gas Factory Junction. Colour-lights were extended via Upminster to Southend Central & East and on to Shoeburyness. Control of this section of track passed from 41 to just eight signalboxes, three being new powerboxes at Barking *(Picture 141)*, Pitsea and Southend Central. Between Barking and Pitsea via Tilbury, a new powerbox was erected at Tilbury Riverside, while 9 of the 21 existing signalboxes were retained with the addition of two new ones.

On both routes, the existing signalboxes were fitted with new panels to operate the signals, leaving the lever frames to operate the points. Between most signalboxes, automatic colour-light signals were provided, but between Low Street and Thames Haven Junction, although colour-lights were installed, they were connected to the mechanical frame and, as continuous track circuiting was not felt to be justified, absolute block working was retained.

The new NX panels varied in design. At Barking, separate rotary entry switches and exit push buttons were provided. At Pitsea and Tilbury, exit buttons doubled as entrance buttons for the advance section as recently standardised in the new powerboxes at Hackney Downs, Broxbourne and Harlow. The panels also differed at the mechanical signalboxes. At Laindon *(Picture 142)*, Leigh and Southend East, for example, each signal had its own switch on the panel (Individual Function Switch Panel — IFS), while other existing signalboxes were fitted with NX panels. On the Tilbury loop, most level crossings were supervised from existing signalboxes, while the remainder were manned by crossing keepers provided with ground frames to operate the colour-light signals.

London Midland Region

Whereas the Euston 1952 resignalling had not been as technologically advanced as it might have been, by the time the resignalling of St Pancras was completed the Region had something a little more progressive to show for its investment of £275,000. The new signalbox was commissioned on 6 October 1957 and was the first panel installed by the London Midland Region *(Pictures 143 & 144)*. It took over the work of St Pancras Passenger signalbox, equipped with two mechanical lever frames facing each other with 32 and 41 levers *(Picture 145)*, St Pancras Junction with 148 levers, Cambridge Street with 18 levers, St Paul's Road Passenger Junction with 34 levers and St Pancras Tunnel, tucked into the wall of the tunnel with just six levers to act as a break-section box. Carlton Road was retained and Dock Junction became the fringe signalbox.

The following year a new powerbox was commissioned at Huddersfield over the weekend of 29/30 November 1958. This contained an IFS panel with 114 switches to

Above (142):
Inside Laindon signalbox, showing part of the mechanical lever frame for working the points, with the IFS panel for operating the colour-light signals above. *BR(E)*

Below (143):
Class 45 No 101 entering St Pancras on 25 August 1972, passing the powerbox of 1957. *D. E. Canning*

operate 196 different routes and took over the work of Huddersfield No 1 and No 2 mechanical signalboxes with a total of 226 levers *(Picture 146)*. From 9 July 1961 the area of its control was extended, so that Springwood and Gledholt Junction signalboxes could be abolished.

During the summer of 1962 a new powerbox at Manchester Victoria East Junction was commissioned with a Westinghouse OCS panel *(Pictures 147 & 148)*. The equipment had been ordered in the 1950s but installation was delayed because resources were concentrated on the West Coast electrification and resignalling. By 1962 NX panels had become the accepted technology and contemporary reports were not afraid to describe the Manchester installation as dated *(Picture 149)*.

Southern Region

After the 1926 signalbox at Cannon Street station was destroyed by fire in April 1957 *(Picture 150)*, the Southern Region quickly had 47 levers of a miniature lever frame up and running in the crew room of the old station signalbox. A new signalbox was commissioned on 15 December 1957 with a Westinghouse 167-miniature lever frame obtained from the LMR, part of a 227-lever frame ordered for the abortive resignalling of Preston station by the LMS in 1939.

The following year, the region's first route-setting panel was installed at Keymer Crossing and on 22 February 1959 the second was brought into use in a new signalbox at Barnes. The new panel was supplied by Westinghouse and was compared at the time to that firm's installation at St Pancras. Mechanical signalboxes were closed at

Putney, Barnes East, Barnes Junction and Barnes Loop Line Crossing.

But both these projects were insignificant when compared with the Southern Region's next modernisation scheme, the Kent Coast electrification. The extension of the third rail dc system from Gillingham to Ramsgate was one of BR's flagship modernisation projects, but before it was completed the £23.5 million project was criticised for being too lavish. Some felt the scheme, which included quadrupling long sections of the route, was not going to show a sufficient return in extra passenger numbers to justify the considerable investment. Heavy engineering work during the project, particularly at St Mary Cray, Shortlands and Gillingham, adding to journey times, only fuelled the complaints.

In Phase 1 of the project, eight new signalboxes were constructed to replace 31 mechanical ones. Shepherds Lane, Brixton opened on 8 March 1959 with a frame of miniature levers and replaced four mechanical boxes in the Brixton, Herne Hill and Loughborough Junction area. The other new signalboxes opened shortly afterwards on 12 April at Beckenham Junction (with a route-setting panel) *(Picture 151)*, Shortlands (with a similar panel), Chislehurst Junction (with a different route-setting panel, replacing seven mechanical signalboxes), Rochester (with a route-setting panel, replacing Chatham Goods Sidings and Chatham Station mechanical signalboxes), Rainham, Sittingbourne (controlling the Sheerness branch with CTC — see Chapter 8) and Faversham. Automatic multi-aspect colour-light signalling was commissioned between Teynham and Westgate between 12 and 26 April 1959 and the first stage of the electrification was inaugurated on 15 June 1959, when electric trains began to run from London to Ramsgate and Dover via Faversham.

The aim of Phase 2 of the project was to extend the colour-light signalling installed by the SR out of Charing Cross and Cannon Street in 1926, southwards from Parks Bridge Junction, Lewisham. Work started between Sevenoaks via Tonbridge and Ashford to Dover, from Ashford via Canterbury West to Ramsgate, from Maidstone East to Ashford

Left (147):
The signal gantry and former L&YR signalbox at Manchester Victoria East Junction, photographed on 8 October 1957. *J. A. Peden (88/7)*

Centre left (148):
The same location in 1962, showing the signal gantry still *in situ* but without the semaphore arms, in front of the new but architecturally incoherent Manchester Victoria East Junction powerbox. *Ian Allan Library*

Below (149):
Part of the OCS panel inside Manchester Victoria East Junction. *BR(LM)*

Above right (150):
The charred remains of the 1926 signalbox at Cannon Street station after the fire of 5 April 1957. *Michael E. Ware*

Centre right (151):
The mechanical signalbox at Beckenham Junction, photographed next to the new replacement powerbox. *P. J. Lynch*

Bottom right (152):
Orpington powerbox photographed by the official BR(S) photographer in 1962. *BR(S)*

and from Maidstone West to Paddock Wood at the end of 1960. Extensive track remodelling took place with the aim of increasing line capacity and headways between trains. Long sections of automatic signalling were installed and, in all, 33 mechanical signalboxes were abolished, another eight retained for shunting purposes though normally closed, and six new powerboxes were erected at Hither Green, Orpington *(Picture 152)*, Sevenoaks, Tonbridge, Ashford and Folkestone Junction, all equipped with NX panels.

Only in Maidstone East signalbox did a new miniature lever frame replace a full-size mechanical frame. Hither Green, replacing seven mechanical signalboxes, was commissioned on 4 February 1962. Folkestone Junction, the first Southern Region powerbox to have a panel made up of individual 'tiles' or 'dominoes' as used on the Western Region (see below), was brought into use on 18 February 1962. Tonbridge powerbox was commissioned on 18 March 1962 and when Ashford powerbox opened in April 1962, Phase 2 of the Kent Coast electrification was complete.

The final Southern Region resignalling project completed by the end of the period covered by this chapter was centred on Guildford. The new powerbox there with the by then standard NX panel was opened over the weekend of 16/17 April 1966 *(Pictures 153 & 154)*. The area of control extended out from Woking to Aldershot, Effingham Junction and Farncombe, and led to the closure of 12 mechanical signalboxes. *Modern Railways* commented in its June 1966 magazine that the work at Guildford was a 'modest installation' compared with current Southern Region plans to run its network from only 30 powerboxes, and the writer went on to say he believed that the region could be controlled from far fewer.

Western Region

The Western Region had achieved very little up to 1955, but once it began its programme

of modernisation, it soon took a lead in new developments. The first of these was the use of a four-number code introduced in 1958 to describe trains in the working timetable. This became the basis for a national system incorporating both numbers and letters two years later. Diesel and electric locomotives displayed the codes in illuminated panels on their fronts and the same codes were displayed by train describers incorporated into the latest signalling panels.

Resignalling work at Birmingham Snow Hill set the standard for future panel construction. New colour-light signalling was commissioned there on 10/11 September 1960, controlled from a new NX panel of rotary switches and buttons with illuminated diagram and train describer boxes above, located in a room within the station.

The panel, supplied by Henry Williams Ltd, was designed by Integra AG of Switzerland and was made up of individual 'tiles' or 'dominoes' as they were sometimes referred to, approximately 2in square. This modular form of creating the track diagram from a standard range of symbols (eg left-hand point, crossover, buffer stop, etc) meant panels no longer had to be tailor-made for each location. The signals on the diagram indicated all aspects, from red through yellow and double yellow to green, depending on what aspect the outdoor signals were displaying. Ironically, despite Snow Hill's pioneering role in panel design, the station's closure along with the ex-GWR lines westwards to Wolverhampton was announced early in 1963.

The next Integra panel came into use in Plymouth's new signalbox on 24-26 November 1960. The resignalling work there had technically begun before World War 2 as part of the complete rebuilding of Plymouth station. Before the station buildings could be completed, however, work was abandoned, but a large mechanical signalbox with 185 levers was finished just before

hostilities broke out in 1939. Resignalling work restarted in a completely different form in September 1957, leading to the closure of six mechanical boxes including the 1939 structure.

The Western Region then turned its attention to resignalling its main line out of Paddington at an estimated cost of £1.5 million. Work started during the summer of 1962 and at the end of the year a new powerbox opened at Twyford. It contained both a state-of-the-art Integra NX panel and a new 56-lever mechanical frame to control local train movements and the Henley-on-Thames branch. A new NX panel was also installed at the same time in the existing 115-lever Reading Main Line East signalbox, so that together with Twyford it controlled colour-light signalling from just east of Reading to just west of Maidenhead, a total of 40 track miles.

Old Oak Common powerbox was commissioned on 8 October 1962 with two NX Integra panels, one for controlling the lines just over two miles from Paddington to the existing colour-light signalling between Southall and Acton and the branches to Wycombe and North Pole Junction, the other to control the engine and carriage lines into Paddington (Picture 155). Provision was made for 209 routes to be set and Old Oak Common East, West and Friars Junction manual signalboxes with a total of 325 levers were abolished.

The next part of this resignalling scheme saw the commissioning on 13 October 1963 of the new powerbox at Slough, containing what had by then become the WR's standard Integra NX panel. As well as the main line, the panel also controlled the branch to Windsor, which was reduced from double to single track. When the next new powerbox opened at Reading in April 1965, complete with NX panel, it was an historically significant event, because Reading Signal Works had been the manufacturer of

countless pieces of traditional GWR mechanical signalling equipment for almost exactly one hundred years. Reading Main Line West Box, constructed in red brick to a unique and proud design in 1896 to house the company's own design of lever frame (initially 185 levers later replaced by one with 222), was closed as part of the resignalling scheme. It survived as an empty reminder until 1988 when it was demolished.

Further west in South Wales, the resignalling in the Newport area, completed at the beginning of 1963, was a hybrid scheme incorporating a new powerbox commissioned at Newport High Street on 8/9 December 1962 and new mechanical signalboxes at Waterloo Loop to the west and East Usk to the east of the station. Fifteen mechanical signalboxes were abolished, as were Newport East and West, which contained the GWR's notable route-setting equipment installed in 1927 and 1928 to the design of R. J. S. Insell and L. M. G. Ferreira. This was followed at the end of 1963 by the opening of a new powerbox at Port Talbot with a standard NX panel. And to complete the resignalling of the main lines in South Wales, a new powerbox was commissioned at Cardiff on 27 March 1966, the most complex area of track so far controlled from a single installation on the Western Region.

West Coast Main Line Resignalling

A child of the 1955 Modernisation Plan of British Railways, the electrification of the West Coast main line was the prestigious project of its period. The spacing of four-aspect colour-light signals to give a 4-5min headway between trains running on green indications, whether travelling at 100mph or 25mph, was one of the initial aims. Extensive

Left (156):
'Crab' No 42828 hurrying a Manchester train past Heaton Norris, still controlled by LNWR lower quadrant semaphores in 1951.
N. F. W. Dyckhoff

Centre left (157):
Inside the 1955 Heaton Norris Junction signalbox shortly after it was brought into use.
BR(LM) D2529

Bottom left (158):
The interior of Wilmslow powerbox when new in 1959. *BR(LM) DM5019*

Right (159):
The interior of Manchester Piccadilly powerbox. When this photograph was taken in August 1960, the illuminated diagram was still inscribed 'Manchester London Road'. *BR(LM)*

track remodelling and the building of new stations were also a major part of the brief. By the time the project was completed in 1966, it was calculated that £175 million had been spent on the electrification, including £42 million on track alterations and resignalling.

Just predating the scheme by a few months, new multi-aspect colour-light signals had been brought into use between Stockport and Levenshulme in March 1955 (*Picture 156*). The existing boxes at Stockport were retained, with a new mechanical box at Heaton Norris (with a standard LMR 120-lever mechanical frame — *Picture 157*) replacing four older structures. With the exception of five sets of points, all points at Heaton Norris were mechanical. Inside the signalbox, the block instruments, telephones, signal repeaters and release plungers were all incorporated into a panel on a traditional block shelf to give the equipment a more modern appearance. But this was purely a cosmetic arrangement. When a block bell rang, a lamp lit up for 10sec to indicate which bell had sounded.

Following this work, the electrification project started in earnest between Manchester and Crewe, and on 13 July 1958 multi-aspect colour-light signals were brought into use on the 9½ miles of line between Wilmslow and Slade Lane Junction. Mechanical signalboxes were closed at Styal, Heald Green, East Didsbury and Mauldeth Road, while the existing signalbox at Wilmslow temporarily controlled signals until the new powerbox was opened there in 1959. This was the first time Westinghouse Brake & Signal Co's 'Westronic' high speed remote control equipment had been used, whereby one wire was used to carry a number of different electrical impulses, or codes, to work a number of pieces of remote equipment.

In June 1959 Sandbach powerbox was brought into use, with Wilmslow ready a few weeks later. The former controlled the line between Chelford and Salop Goods Junction (Crewe) with a Westinghouse route-setting panel of the one control switch (OCS) type. The main line signals were usually automatically controlled from the track

circuits, the signalman taking control only when movements across the through routes were necessary. Telephones were provided at all the 53 multi-aspect colour-light signals. Satellite relay interlocking centres included installations at Sydney Bridge, Rookery Bridge, Holmes Chapel and Goostrey, each connected to Sandbach by the Westronic system.

The new powerbox at Wilmslow (also with an OCS panel) controlled the line from Chelford to Cheadle Hulme, 15 route miles of double track *(Picture 158)*. Both boxes were manned by a signalman and traffic controller. Twenty-seven mechanical signalboxes were abolished and a further six downgraded to electrically-released ground frames or unmanned installations remotely controlled from the powerboxes.

The illuminated diagrams above the panels in both boxes also displayed the trains' four-character description codes recently introduced on BR. Once set up, the code moved automatically between description boxes as the train progressed across the diagram. (The LMR officially introduced its four-character headcodes at the beginning of the summer timetable of 1961.)

Only a few months after Sandbach and Wilmslow powerboxes opened, BR was already reassessing its commitment to future work. Between 1959 and 1963 the mileage it had hoped to resignal was to be cut by a third and further resignalling work on the West Coast main line was modified to reduce costs and speed up completion of the project.

Originally it had been planned to construct 45 new power signalboxes to control the line between London Euston, Liverpool and Manchester, but the modified plans envisaged far fewer with certain mechanical signalboxes retained.

Another milestone was reached in August 1960, when on the 28th of that month the new powerbox at Manchester Piccadilly (formerly London Road) was fully commissioned, replacing the power-signalling installations of the former GCR and LNWR. The four stages of the work had started in 1958 and the new panel controlled lines to Mayfield station, from Oxford Road to Heaton Chapel, to Gatley, to Ashburys and to Midland Junction on the Philips Park line. The work of 13 signalboxes with a total of 848 levers (including miniature levers and slides) was taken over by the new powerbox. Eleven of those old boxes were abolished, and two downgraded to shunting frames. The new powerbox was manned by three signalmen and a regulator per shift *(Picture 159)*. The OCS panel was 47ft long and capable of setting up 491 routes. The illuminated diagram had built-in train describers above the console, the codes being set up with push buttons rather than by using telephone dials as in contemporary Western Region installations.

The Manchester powerbox directly controlled all signalling within a mile of the station but beyond that five satellite relay interlocking rooms were built at Longsight North, Longsight South, Slade Lane Junction,

Mauldeth Road and East Didsbury. Slade Lane had been provided with its own panel in 1958 and, after the new powerbox was commissioned, this was retained for use in emergencies. All signals were multi-aspect and there were 192 points operated electro-pneumatically.

The Manchester resignalling was the culmination of the first phase of the electrification project, and a fortnight after its completion, on 12 September 1960, a full electric train service was introduced between Crewe and Manchester.

Work then focused on the lines southwards towards London Euston. For future work, including new powerboxes planned at Coventry, Edge Hill, Weaver Junction, Stoke-on-Trent, Norton Bridge and Nuneaton, it was decided that NX panels would be used instead of the OCS types installed at Manchester, Sandbach and Wilmslow.

Weaver Junction signalbox opened in March 1961 *(Picture 160)*, followed in August by the commissioning of the new powerbox at Edge Hill, Liverpool, incorporating a Westinghouse NX panel *(Picture 161)*. Miniaturisation of the panel's components meant a very compact design compared with the large consoles at Wilmslow and Sandbach. Ironically the panel was criticised in a *Trains Illustrated* article for being *too* compact — so much so that the traffic regulator seated behind the signalman could not see the small train descriptions displayed in the diagram. It was also suggested that the signalmen had difficulty

Above (160):
Weaver Junction was intended to be a temporary powerbox, which explains why the operating floor, although above the relay room, was in fact physically separated from it. Notice the wire mesh around the colour-light signal units, intended to protect S&T staff from the high voltage overhead cables.
BR(LM) D4438

Below (161):
The compact NX panel at Edge Hill.
Westinghouse Brake & Signal Co

seeing the descriptions because of light reflecting on the panel from the outside. At that time, the Eastern Region was incorporating overhanging roofs into its new signalboxes to act as sun baffles, and it was suggested the LMR should do the same. When the new powerbox at Norton Bridge opened on 8 October 1961, it sported just such an overhanging canopy.

During May 1962 the new station at Coventry opened. Reconstruction work which started in January 1958 included extensive track remodelling and the provision of a new powerbox commissioned 14-16 April 1962. The new panel was of the NX push-button type with individual point switches for emergency use and an illuminated diagram incorporating the train description displays above. The new box took over the work of Coventry's four manual signalboxes and led to the downgrading to a shunting frame of Whitley Wharf box.

The work at Coventry had remained true to the original 1950s electrification concept, but six months later the pragmatic and more cost-conscious version from a less certain management was revealed. On 10/- 11 November 1962 colour-light signalling between Lichfield and Nuneaton on the Trent Valley line was brought into use but although the work led to the abolition of four mechanical signalboxes, the new signalling was connected up to the existing ex-LNWR lever frames in the remaining boxes. The only new signalboxes to be erected were at Colwich Junction and Atherstone, the latter replacing the overhead structure. Both boxes were a generation removed from the work at Coventry, Norton Bridge and Edge Hill, with mechanical lever frames for point operation and panels to control the signals.

Existing mechanical signalboxes were also retained at Stafford, where the Trent Valley line rejoined the Birmingham route. Stafford No 5 boasted a frame of 150 levers, and the only recently completed No 4 signalbox of 1960 contained a 105-lever frame. Between there and Crewe and northwards to Weaver Junction a mixture of ex-LNWR and ex-LMS mechanical signalboxes continued in use but despite this compromise by May 1962 continuous track circuiting and colour-light

signalling extended southwards from Manchester as far as Stafford, and on 7 January 1963 a limited electric service was run between there and Crewe.

By the end of 1963, optimism had returned to the West Coast project. Work on a new generation of powerboxes between Nuneaton and Euston was in hand and at the beginning of October 1963 Nuneaton powerbox was successfully brought into use *(Picture 162)*. Six months later the contract was let to rebuild Birmingham New Street station, which would include the LMR's showpiece powerbox. Then in July 1964 the first of the large powerboxes south of Nuneaton opened at Watford *(Picture 163)*, controlling the quadruple track between North Wembley signalbox, nine miles from Euston, and Cheddington signalbox, 36 miles from the capital. Ten mechanical signalboxes were abolished as a result, although ground frames released from the new powerbox were provided at all seven stations between Harrow & Wealdstone and Cheddington, for shunting and the control of crossovers. The new NX Watford panel was the most compact so far installed on the LMR, just 8ft long to control 112 track miles (28 route miles). A separate illuminated diagram with train describers was provided, easily visible to the train regulators seated behind the signalman.

Between 14 and 28 September 1964, the new powerbox was brought into use at Rugby *(Pictures 164 & 165)*, controlling 59 route miles, at the time the longest area under the control of just one installation. To complete the resignalling into London, NX panels were commissioned at Bletchley, Willesden and Euston in June, July and September 1965 respectively. Willesden, Bletchley and Rugby panels were all supplied by SGE Railway Signals, the unit at Willesden capable of setting 322 routes. Strategically placed satellite interlockings were provided; those controlled from Willesden, for example, were located at Kenton, Wembley, Willesden South and Queens Park. As at Watford there were ground frames at various places, released from the relevant powerbox, and around Willesden, although 11 existing manual signalboxes were abolished, a number were retained as shunting frames. Unusually, trains between Willesden powerbox and Mitre Bridge Junction signalbox were still controlled using absolute block, the indications on the former's panel being indicated by coloured lights, the indications and bell codes being transmitted by push-buttons.

The panel at Euston was supplied by Westinghouse and took over the work of the 227-miniature lever frame installed only 13 years before. Although the panel controlled the smallest track area of all the new powerboxes, it was capable of setting 755 routes in and around the station and needed two signalmen to operate it, supported by the area controller, train recorder and train announcer.

The final pieces of the West Coast resignalling were put into place in the West Midlands and at Stoke-on-Trent. New powerboxes were completed at Walsall and Wolverhampton at the end of 1965, the latter with a Westinghouse NX panel commissioned on 16 August. Sixteen mechanical signalboxes were closed as a result, with a further six downgraded to shunting frames. The culmination of the whole West Coast electrification and resignalling was the completion of Stoke-on-Trent and Birmingham New Street powerboxes, a little after the full electric service between London, Crewe, Liverpool and Manchester had been launched on 18 April 1966.

The Stoke-on-Trent NX panel brought into use in July was the last new powerbox commissioned as part of the West Coast modernisation but it was the installation at Birmingham which attracted the most comment. It was commissioned in three stages: Stage 1 became operational during January 1966; Stage 2 during June, and the final Stage 3 on 3 July 1966. Built in a style completely different from its contemporaries, the signalbox structure, emerging from the depths of the northern approaches to the station like a giant armoured tower, was an impressive and uncompromising architectural monument to 1960s confidence and optimism *(Picture 166)*. The Westinghouse NX panel at Birmingham was capable of setting 400 routes. When the new signalbox at York had been commissioned over a decade before in 1951, it had been capable of setting over twice that many routes, but whereas that led to the closure of eight mechanical signalboxes with a total of 867 levers, the Birmingham panel took over the work of 38 mechanical signalboxes with a total of 1,285 levers. Birmingham New Street station and its signalbox epitomised and continues to epitomise British Railways' great era of modernisation.

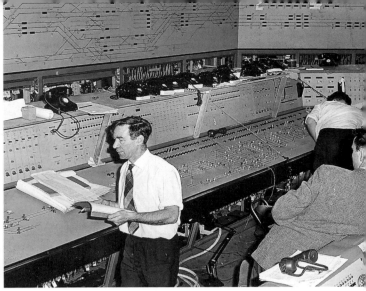

6 More of the Same 1966-87

After 1955, modernisation had become almost synonymous with electrification and resignalling with multi-aspect colour-light signals. But following the completion of the West Coast main line modernisation in 1966, there were no other projects on such a large scale which included both elements in the same scheme. The extension of overhead wires to Glasgow in the 1970s and the electrification of the East Coast main line a decade later were both preceded by resignalling. The only significant resignalling schemes carried out concurrently with electrification were the London suburban improvements out of St Pancras and King's Cross.

For main lines, electrification was no longer the unquestioned way to improve services. From 1966 and throughout the 1970s, the Eastern Region upgraded track and signalling piecemeal, pushing its fleet of 'Deltic' diesel locomotives to their operational limits *(Picture 167)*. At the end of that decade, with the introduction of the diesel-powered IC125s (or HSTs — High Speed Trains), services on the Western Region main line out of Paddington and on the East Coast route were transformed, all achieved without costly electrification.

But if electrification schemes stalled in the 1970s, resignalling projects did manage to continue. The beginning of the decade witnessed the completion of some very impressive ones and what distinguishes the work of the 1970s and 1980s from that of the previous decades is the extent of the areas controlled from single powerboxes. Improvements in technology, most notably electronic remote control and component miniaturisation, meant there was almost no limit to the areas new powerboxes could control. The comments in the June 1966 *Modern Railways*, referred to in the last chapter, that the Southern Region could be operated from far fewer than the planned 30 new powerboxes, were answered in August that year by none other than the Region's Chief S&T Engineer, J. F. H. Tyler. He remarked that it was both theoretically and technically possible to control the network from only three control centres, although practically this could not be achieved.

Nevertheless, in 1969 the Southern Region announced it wanted to concentrate control in just 13 powerboxes and in the next few years went a long way to achieving this goal.

When resignalling of the West Coast route northwards to Glasgow was authorised in 1969 only four powerboxes were planned to control over 200 miles of track, and in August 1970 *Railway Magazine* devoted a whole article to the progress of resignalling in this country, commenting that British Railways was beginning to see such projects in a national context and not just on a regional basis.

Perhaps one of the main reasons resignalling projects were easier to justify compared to electrification schemes, was that once commissioned they brought about immediate savings. In 1969, for example, the commissioning of Trent, Derby and Saltley powerboxes led to the closure of nearly 200 mechanical signalboxes out of a total of 510 closures throughout the country. To a cost-conscious government, the reduction of staff that this meant was a distinct bonus. But the elimination of signalboxes was not seen as an advantage by many railwaymen. During the period covered by this chapter there were heated debates about the long distances that trains were travelling without being observed by signalmen, or in fact by any railway staff. To traditional signalmen, trained to observe the passing of every train in case doors were

open, loads not properly secured, axle-boxes overheating or, worse still, trains divided or running away, it was very hard to accept the new ways of operating a railway.

At the end of 1966, BR announced that it was to install hot-box detectors in areas of colour-light signalling controlled by widely spaced powerboxes, but there were still dissenting voices. The increased use of automatic half barriers at level crossings caused considerable public debate, these issues being outlined in Chapter 10. If the amount of freight on the railways had not declined so dramatically in the 1970s, and unfitted trains had continued to run, perhaps railwaymen's and the public's fears would have been justified. But modern signalling practices eventually became more than adequate to control safely a drastically rationalised British Railways network, traversed by fewer, and mainly fixed-formation, trains than in mechanical signalling days.

There is no doubt that this period witnessed the biggest cull of mechanical signalboxes in the history of railway signalling. As well as the many hundreds referred to in this chapter, hundreds more were closed. The scale of closures means that this narrative at times reads more like a list than a history. As with the period 1945-66, it is impossible to record all the changes between 1966 and 1987. But hopefully what

Right (167):
Apart from the substitution of upper quadrant arms for the original GNR somersault ones, the signalling at Harringay in this June 1972 view was the same as when *Dominion of New Zealand* was photographed there hauling the 'Silver Jubilee' before World War 2 *(Picture 68)*. 'Deltic' No 9010 *The King's Own Scottish Borderer* on a down King's Cross-Aberdeen train. *P. A. Dobson*

resignalling schemes are mentioned here will show how, gradually and painfully, British Railways cast off its considerable Victorian legacy. In 1966 the majority of the network was still fundamentally as the Victorian engineers had left it; by 1987, for better or for worse, it was an entirely different organisation.

This chapter considers its chosen period in three chronological subdivisions, with a concluding piece on the East Coast main line. First, 1966-9; the final year was chosen because the commissioning of Trent, Derby and Saltley powerboxes emphatically marked the end of a remarkable decade. Then 1970-4; the period when powerboxes became 'signalling centres' and their areas of control became truly extensive: 1974 was the year when passengers could catch an electric train in London Euston and be in Glasgow only 5hr later. Finally, 1975-87; the period when a number of 'modernisation' schemes and

powerboxes of the 1950s and 60s were superseded and when signalling truly entered the computer age with the development of Radio Electronic Token Block (RETB) working (described in Chapter 8), Solid-State Interlocking (SSI) and finally the development of the Integrated Electronic Control Centre (IECC).

Between 1966 and 1980, the basic signalling technology standardised by the mid-1960s did not change; it was simply a case of more of the same. The development of the reed relay, or Type RR Remote Control System, at the end of the 1960s, did lead towards the elimination of satellite inter-lockings, but the fundamental change came in the early 1980s when engineers brought their experiments with solid state electronics — computers — into practical use.

In 1985 Leamington Spa was resignalled and controlled from a panel, the integrity of whose interlocking was dependent on a

computer. With the introduction of this technology, the last link with mechanical signalling, the electro-mechanical relay, was eliminated. Two years later, development work began to take computerised signalling control a stage further with the creation of the Integrated Electronic Control Centre (IECC). It was the most fundamental change in signalling technology since before World War 2.

Resignalling Schemes 1966-9

Scottish Resignalling Projects

By 1966, £30 million had already been earmarked for resignalling projects in

Left (168):
The NX panel and illuminated diagram at Leeds. *John Lawrence*

Right (169):
The powerbox at Portsmouth, constructed using a number of standard concrete sections. Photographed on 3 March 1968. *John H. Bird*

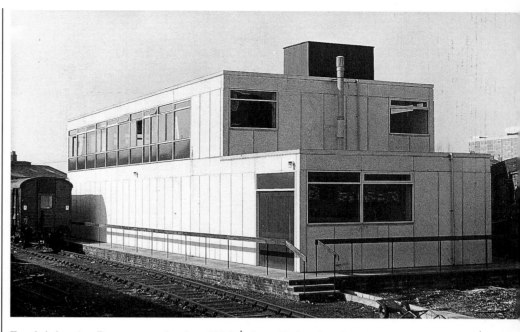

Scotland. Work had started with the construction of a new powerbox at Paisley which, with an extension of the area of Glasgow Central's control and the upgrading of Gourock signalbox, extended colour-light signalling as far west as Wemyss Bay. In the summer of 1967, the Glasgow South Bank electrification was completed and on 5 June a new electric passenger service started to run. A new panel was installed at Glasgow Central powerbox, the remainder of the line to Gourock and Wemyss Bay being controlled from the new powerbox at Paisley.

Leeds Remodelling and Resignalling

It had been announced at the end of the 1950s that all passenger traffic in Leeds would be concentrated on a rebuilt City station allowing Leeds Central to be closed, but although work started in October 1959, the project was substantially altered with much more rationalisation of track before completion in 1967. The LNER signalboxes of 1936/7 were closed and the rebuilt City station opened in May 1967, part of the buildings incorporating a room for the new signalling panel supplied by Westinghouse. The installation comprised a separate console with illuminated diagram above *(Picture 168)*. One feature which led to comment in the contemporary railway press was the use of a computer to store, check and transmit the train descriptions. Apart from the handling of the numbers, the action of the descriptions moving automatically across the diagram as the train progressed was no different from existing systems. (The computer was not fully operational until the summer of 1968.) Despite the rationalisation of track, the new panel was capable of setting 520 routes, its area of control covering 47 track miles. Seventeen mechanical signalboxes were closed as a result.

Southern Region Resignalling

Plans for new powerboxes at Guildford, Portsmouth and Eastleigh to replace life-expired equipment had been put forward for approval by the Southern Region of BR in the summer of 1963. Guildford has already been mentioned in the previous chapter and in June 1966 a new NX panel was commissioned in the 1937 Woking signalbox as part of the Bournemouth resignalling project. This was followed in November 1966 by the opening of new powerboxes at Basingstoke and Eastleigh. At Bournemouth the 1928 mechanical signalbox with its 60-lever frame was retained to operate the new colour-light signals there. Semaphores remained at Brockenhurst and Christchurch, but otherwise new multi-aspect colour-light signalling extended from Woking to St Denys, Botley and Andover Junction.

The panels in all the new powerboxes were the by then standard Integra-type NX pattern with four-character train describers. It was noted at the time that they were some of the first such tile, domino or mosaic panels made and supplied by Westinghouse. At Basingstoke, prewired relays of the Westpac Mark 2 type were used. Between them, the new powerboxes, including the panel in Woking, controlled 70 route miles of main line. Basingstoke panel was capable of setting 130 routes and Eastleigh 224. The resignalling led to the closure of 25 signalboxes, a number (Winchester, for example) having been built only a few years previously as part of an earlier resignalling scheme.

Of note in the Bournemouth resignalling project was the use of junction indicators with a row of five white lights. These were the first to be used on the Southern Region, which hitherto had used three white lights above the main signal aspect to indicate a diverging route. Their use brought the Region in line with others on BR.

Of historical interest was the elimination in November 1966 of the last remains of the LSWR's 1902 automatic signalling between Farnborough and Basingstoke. Originally the LSWR's installation had extended as far as Woking, but much of this had disappeared in the resignalling of 1937.

Resignalling between Portsmouth Harbour and Portcreek, Farlington and Cosham Junction (with automatic signals between Farlington and Havant) was completed in the summer of 1968. Because of the uncertainty about the continued use of automatic half barrier (ahb) level crossings (see Chapter 10), Green Lanes Crossing south of Hilsea Halt retained its signalbox to control the gates there. Eight other signalboxes were abolished. The scope of the Portsmouth powerbox was described at the time as 'limited by modern standards', the panel controlling just 20 track miles and capable of setting 183 routes *(Picture 169)*.

Paddington and Swindon Resignalling

At the end of 1966, Westinghouse secured the contract to provide remote control and other equipment for resignalling around Swindon, and for the upgrading of the existing colour-light signalling between Paddington and Dawley (Hayes). The latter scheme involved the remodelling of the layout at Paddington, including the complete segregation of the London Transport lines from the Western Region's ones approaching and within the station, and the commissioning of a new powerbox at Old Oak Common in 1967/8. It was the first time a London terminus had been controlled from a signalbox remote from the station and it was a considerable achievement for the region. The new powerbox at Old Oak Common was built next to the existing 1962 structure which was retained, its relay room used for its original purpose while the old operating floor became the District Inspector's office.

Although the resignalling was impressive, there were questions as to why the 1962 powerbox had lasted so short a time. G. M. Kitchenside, writing in *Modern Railways* for March 1969, justified this by saying that it was not due to bad planning by the region, but due to the 'rapid advance of remote control technology in the last few years'.

Outwardly the new NX panel was little different from its 1962 predecessor, being made up of individual Integra tiles and standard push-buttons. But what was different was the number of individual pieces of equipment operated from the box and the area of its control; 279 colour-light signals; 171

Left (170):
Just some of the relays inside Swindon powerbox. BR(W) 48356/7

point machines; 13¾ route and 67¼ track miles and a possible 688 routes compared with the 209 of the old powerbox. Eighteen ex-GWR signalboxes which had been controlling colour-light signals since the 1953 and 1962 resignallings were abolished under the new scheme.

Resignalling of the main line further west between Challow and Corsham was commissioned in the same year. The new streamlined railway, devoid of its intermediate stations and sidings, was controlled from a new powerbox at Swindon, its control extending along branches to Badminton and to Kemble on the recently-singled Gloucester route. Twenty-eight mechanical signalboxes were closed and the job of looking out for overheated axleboxes placed in the care of one Servo hot-box detector near Hay Lane between Wootton Bassett and Swindon. Extensive rationalisation of the layout at Swindon was also part of the scheme, so that to many traditional railwaymen the vital statistics of the new powerbox were not impressive — the control of 87¾ route miles, 197 routes, 107 running signals, 69 shunting signals and 79 point machines (*Picture 170*).

London Midland Region resignalling

The most impressive resignalling scheme of the 1960s, and a fitting conclusion to the decade, was undoubtedly that centred on the new powerboxes at Trent just southwest of Nottingham, at Derby and at Saltley outside Birmingham. It was by far the largest resignalling project undertaken in one go and over lines not destined for electrification. The area affected stretched from Chesterfield in the north, to Nottingham, Moira West, Abbey Junction (Nuneaton) and Leamington Spa in the east, to Blackwell on the Birmingham main line to Bristol in the south, a total of 242 route miles and 597 track miles, most of it former MR territory. A total of 745 new colour-light signals were erected, 357 of which were automatic or semi-automatic, and there were a total of 1,620 individual controlled track circuits.

The contracts were awarded at the end of 1966; AEI-General Signals Ltd for Trent and Saltley, and Westinghouse for Derby. Work started the following year with extensive remodelling and rationalisation of track layouts. The junctions at Trent, Bordesley, Tyseley and many other places were completely altered and ultimately 180 mechanical signalboxes were replaced, only 23 remaining as shunting frames (*Picture 171*). Hot axlebox detectors were installed at various locations.

Structurally the three new powerboxes were long, low, two-storey buildings, the relay rooms being brick clad with no ornamentation (*Picture 172*). Trent boasted the largest operating floor, supporting an NX panel 56ft long in five sections, capable of setting 605 routes. Derby's panel could set 472 routes, and Saltley's 408. At Trent and Saltley satellite interlockings were eliminated by the first extensive use of the reed system of remote control. By comparison, Derby used the by then conventional approach, which needed the use of nine satellite interlockings.

Commissioning of the three powerboxes started in June 1969 with Derby fully operational first. Saltley followed and then, its first stage having opened on 27 September, Trent was finally completed on 8 December 1969. It was said at the time that the area controller, two controllers, one train recorder and four signalmen per shift at Trent had to deal with approaching 250 passenger and over 300 through freight trains daily and additional trip working to and from Toton yard only a few miles away. It must have been a difficult learning curve for signalmen more used to controlling limited sections of track.

Gloucester Resignalling

At the southern end of Saltley's control area between Barnt Green and Blackwell, where the London Midland Region joined the Western Region, resignalling was continued by the latter through to Gloucester. The structure of the new powerbox there was completed by the beginning of 1967 and, like its contemporaries in the Midlands, it was commissioned in the last half of 1969 (*Picture 173*). Standard equipment both by the lineside and in the new powerbox was installed, and there was the usual extensive track rationalisation. There were, however, a number of aspects worthy of note at Gloucester. Originally the whole of the double track line from Swindon to Standish Junction (the Golden Valley line) was to be singled, this having already been achieved on the section between Swindon and Kemble as part of the Swindon resignalling (see previous page). But a reassessment of traffic flows led to the retention of double line from Standish to Kemble.

Two unusual features of the Gloucester resignalling were both due to the continued use of traditional operating procedures for working freight trains up and down the Lickey Incline between Bromsgrove and

Above (171):
The MR tumbler frame inside Derby Station North signalbox, a few years before it was closed. *R. K. Blencowe (33474)*

Right (172):
The new powerbox at Derby, photographed shortly before it was commissioned. *BR(LM)*

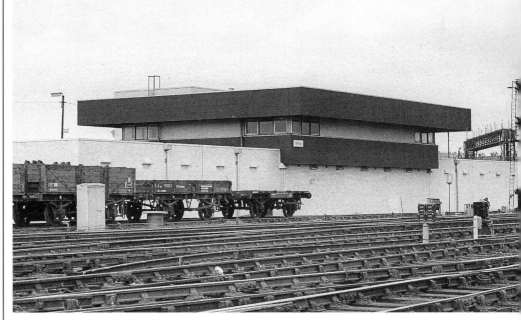

Blackwell. At this time many freights were still banked up the incline and as BR still ran unfitted wagons, those descending the Lickey had to be stopped at Blackwell to have their brakes 'pinned down'. Once the banking engine was positioned at the rear of an ascending train, the driver pressed one of several plungers alongside the up loop at Bromsgrove. This illuminated a white light visible to the driver of the train engine, who then pressed a plunger next to his cab lighting a 'train ready to start' indication in Gloucester powerbox. The signalman then set the route and after 15sec the signal cleared. For those freights descending from Blackwell, the Gloucester signalman was informed by telephone that brakes had been applied before he cleared the appropriate signal to let the train descend.

As part of the Gloucester resignalling, three hot axlebox detectors were installed, one on the down line at Churchdown, one on the up line at Haresfield and one on the up line to Newport. Many level crossings in the area were to have been converted to automatic half barriers (ahbs) but as the Hixon Report had not yet been published (see Chapter 10), this work was postponed and traditional gates were retained. Crossing keepers, in touch with the signalmen at Gloucester, used Annett's keys to release the gates, the key once withdrawn keeping the

signals at danger. The area of Gloucester control extended over 94¾ route miles and 181¾ track miles.

Resignalling Schemes 1970-4

Newport and Bristol Resignalling

As work at Gloucester was being completed, resignalling schemes at Bristol and Newport were also in hand, all planned to link with

each other. By the end of 1969, the area of Newport powerbox's control had been extended through the Severn Tunnel. Colour-light signals were provided inside the tunnel to achieve two sections in each direction (in contrast to the one absolute block section on the up and down lines under mechanical signalling), but as some freight trains were still not fully fitted at this time, the intermediate signals had to be 'off' before such trains entered the tunnel, to give them a clear run through.

The work at Bristol was claimed at the time to be the largest modernisation scheme anywhere in Europe and was organised in 12 separate stages. Remodelling of the track layout at the station started in February 1970,

the Region's list of 13 powerboxes, but was seen as an interim installation prior to Waterloo being commissioned.

By the time Surbiton was complete, Dartford powerbox was under construction. When that panel was commissioned on 1 November 1970, 31 mechanical signalboxes were eliminated. The grant for the Feltham resignalling followed at the end of 1970 and erection of the new powerbox there started at the end of 1972. The first stage was completed on 8 September 1974, followed by full commissioning on 5 October 1974. Eleven level crossings were fitted with full barriers, supervised by closed-circuit television and operated from the new panel, while 45 mechanical signalboxes were closed and the last semaphores in southwest London were displaced.

London Bridge Resignalling

The third new powerbox in the Southern Region's 1969 plan was erected at London Bridge *(Picture 174)*. The aim was to control all trains in and out of not only London Bridge Central terminus and the through platforms (London Bridge South Eastern), but also Charing Cross and Cannon Street stations, improving the flow of traffic through Borough Market Junction. Erecting the structure of the new powerbox began in 1972, and resignalling was well in hand when government approval was given for the rebuilding of the station in the summer of 1974. Between 5 August and 6 September 1974 Cannon Street station was closed to all traffic so that the whole track layout could be completely remodelled. In July the following year the first part of the new panel was commissioned. The last stage of resignalling was completed between 15 and 20 April 1976, when Charing Cross, Cannon Street and Waterloo (East) stations were closed in order to complete the final track layouts and signal placings.

and by March the first stage of the resignalling, controlled from a new powerbox next to Brunel's original Temple Meads station, was operational. Unlike the GWR resignalling scheme of 1935 which had accompanied the enlargement of the station and the laying of many additional lines, the aim in 1970 was to reduce the layout considerably. By this time the report on the Hixon accident had been published, and due to its recommendations the costs of the ahbs installed in the Bristol area had increased by 400%.

In August 1970 the most important stage of the project was reached (Stage 5) when the Bristol panel was finally linked with the one at Swindon, thereby completing an unbroken chain of multi-aspect colour-light signalling and full track circuiting all the way from Paddington via Reading to Bristol. The final stage was completed over the weekend of 18-20 March 1972, when Highbridge Crossing, Huntspill and Bridgwater signalboxes were closed, linking Bristol with Cogload Junction, Taunton, the furthest west the resignalling was planned to extend.

The final statistics of Bristol were certainly impressive for their time: a panel capable of setting 678 routes; the control of 114 route and 254 track miles with 163 running, and 117 automatic signals; 243 point machines and 556 track circuits.

Southern Region Resignalling

At the very end of the 1960s the Southern Region unveiled its £217 million proposals to upgrade services throughout its area. The aim was to control the region from 13 powerboxes at Waterloo, Victoria, London Bridge, Feltham, Basingstoke, Guildford, Eastleigh, East Croydon, Brighton, Dartford, Chislehurst Junction, Gillingham and Ashford (Kent). By then a number of the proposals were already taking shape. The first stage of the Surbiton resignalling was commissioned on 20 April 1969 and completed a year later on 28 February/1 March 1970. This was not on

West Coast Main Line to Glasgow

Authorisation of the resignalling between Weaver Junction and Glasgow was announced in April 1969, with new powerboxes planned at Warrington, Preston, Carlisle and Motherwell. It is interesting to note that the LMS had plans early in 1939 to build two new 'power signalboxes' at Preston, only to have those plans shelved indefinitely during and after War World 2 *(Picture 175)*. Thirty-one years later in the spring of 1970 work started on Preston and Warrington powerboxes, shortly after the official announcement on 23 February 1970 that government money would be available to extend electrification to Glasgow.

The shell of Motherwell powerbox, by then described as a Train Control & Signalling Centre, was completed in the summer of 1971. The NX panel in Warrington, supplied by Westinghouse, was commissioned during September and October 1972, closely followed by the replacement of the 1961 panel in Glasgow Central powerbox and the commissioning of the new NX one on 22 October 1972. On 17 December that year the initial stage of Motherwell powerbox was completed (equipped by GEC-General Signal Ltd) and on the first weekend in February 1973, control of the signalling around Preston station was transferred to the new Westinghouse NX panel there. Carlisle followed in the summer *(Picture 176)*, and full commissioning of all the signalling was achieved in time for the introduction of a full electrified passenger service between London and Glasgow on 6 May 1974 (see below).

The changes in train times were dramatic. The 'Royal Scot', with one stop at Preston, was timetabled to travel between London and Glasgow in just 5hr, while six other services were booked to complete the journey in 5hr 10min, compared with 5min short of 6hr before electrification. Once again the West Coast main line had something to celebrate, O. S. Nock writing in the May edition of *Railway Magazine* that he believed 1974 might '...become regarded as one of the greatest milestones in the long history of British passenger train services'. The realities of the first few months of the new timetable were not faultless, however, Nock observing later that year that problems had been encountered in Scotland, traceable, he thought, to faulty regulation in Motherwell powerbox, staff being unfamiliar '...with traffic working on a scale never previously experienced by those brought up in a lifetime of manual block signalling'. It is rare to find such a perceptive comment in articles by other contemporary writers and it puts into perspective the tremendous changes that had occurred in signalling in just a few decades.

	manual signalboxes abolished	colour-light signals	signalled routes	point machines	track circuits	route miles	track miles
Warrington	39	254	492	232	592	62	145
Preston	87	466	886	364	1,050	114	263
Carlisle	35	325	553	229	874	114	221
Motherwell	91	545	741	329	881	123	277
Glasgow Central	13	147	253	120	223	19	39

Resignalling Schemes 1975-87

Until the 1970s, the aim of signalling and civil engineers was to provide BR with track and signalling systems capable of dealing with trains running up to 100mph. But at the beginning of the new decade, plans for high speed trains were well advanced, and in the early 1970s both the Western and Eastern Regions began to upgrade various sections of their main line for the possibility of running trains at 125mph.

On 5 May 1975, British Rail's prototype High Speed Train started revenue-earning passenger service on the WR main line between Paddington, Bristol and Weston-super-Mare and from 4 October 1976 production units were put into service on this route. It was the first main line in the country on which passenger trains could run up to 125mph and the improvements in the service were revolutionary, perhaps more so than on the West Coast main line two years earlier.

Additional Aspects

Despite the increased speed possible with the HSTs, the basic signalling philosophy based around four aspects was not changed. The only area where a better safety margin was thought necessary was at high speed junctions. At slow speed turnouts, the junction signal remained at danger until the approaching train had occupied the berth track circuit sufficiently long to ensure its speed had been checked. At junctions where higher speeds were permitted, the signal beyond the junction was held at danger, while the junction signal itself showed a single yellow. In this case, with better braking, it was feared that HST drivers might travel too fast through the junction itself while preparing to stop at the red aspect beyond. It was agreed that the solution to this was to precede the yellow junction indication with a flashing double yellow and/or a flashing single yellow. In addition, an alteration was made to the way in which the signal beyond the junction was cleared. It remained at danger until the approaching train had passed over the AWS ramp of the junction signal. The first flashing yellows were installed at Ruscombe near Twyford and at Didcot East Junctions.

Victoria and Three Bridges Signalling Centres

By the mid-1970s, the Southern Region's 1969 plan for 13 powerboxes had been amended to take account of new technology, changing operating practices and financial constraints. Once again hybrid schemes were back on the agenda, and plans for a powerbox at Brighton to control lines as far apart as

Above (176):
The interior of Carlisle No 5 signalbox south of the station. This box opened in 1951 with a mechanical frame of 114 levers and closed when the new powerbox was commissioned in 1973. The block instruments on the shelf nearest the camera were built into a single cabinet making use of traditional LNWR-type tappers and bells suspended beneath the case but substituting the usual single-needle indications for 'line blocked', 'line clear' or 'train on line' with coloured lights. This was just one of a number of abortive attempts to modernise the design of block instruments in the 1950s. *Ian Allan Library*

Hastings, Horsham and Chichester were abandoned. Nevertheless, in the summer of 1976 approval was gained for the resignalling of Victoria station and lines in south London. But instead of building a new powerbox at Victoria as planned, the new signalling centre was to be built at Clapham Junction and because its area of control was to be larger that originally envisaged, plans for an East Croydon powerbox were shelved at the same time. At the end of 1977, GEC-General Signal won the contract to equip six relay rooms in Stages 1 and 2 of this project at Victoria station itself, at Clapham Junction, Stewarts Lane, Balham and Streatham Junction.

Two years later in March 1979 came approval for the £45 million resignalling of the Brighton line and routes to Faygate, Tattenham Corner, Caterham and

Woldingham, to be controlled from a new signalling centre at Three Bridges.

By the end of August 1979, Stage 1 of the Victoria resignalling was complete, covering the South Eastern side of the station. The controlling panel was housed temporarily in the old central signalbox, leading to the closure of the South Eastern signalbox. This was followed in the last weekend in June 1981 by the commissioning of Stage 2 of the new powerbox next to Clapham Junction, completing control of the whole of Victoria station and lines out to Brixton, Clapham, Streatham Hill, Norbury, Tooting and Mitcham Junction. Full commissioning finally took place on 1 May 1984 *(Picture 177)*.

In March 1980, Westinghouse had secured the Three Bridges resignalling project and at the beginning of 1982 work began on remodelling the track layout south of East Croydon station. This was a complex task and included the building of two new bridges and substantial approach embankments. As with all resignalling projects at this time, the changeover was phased in over a number of years. The first stage was commissioned during 1983 and included in the signalling centre at Three Bridges a new piece of equipment that was to become one of the important building blocks in the development of the Integrated Electronic Control Centre (IECC — see next chapter). It was Automatic Route Setting (ARS), and as its name implies it was capable of setting up routes for trains without the intervention of the signalman. The equipment would monitor the progress of trains through its control area, compare this with timetable information, and clear passages for them automatically. Built into the system was the capability of dealing with trains not running to timetable, the ARS checking for alternative routes if any conflicts arose. At any time the signalman could intervene and override the system.

When East Croydon and Gloucester Road Junction signalboxes closed on 7 April, followed by Norwood Junction box on 28 April 1984, Three Bridges began working to Victoria signalling centre. The displaced signalboxes were almost exactly 30 years old, having opened on 24 March 1954. The following year Three Bridges' area of control finally reached Brighton. In April the 1932 signalbox there was closed, after a disastrous fire, followed by Redhill A and B signalboxes in May 1985. Oxted became a fringe box in November that year, when Sanderstead, Upper Warlingham and Woldingham signalboxes were closed , and the Three Bridges control area was finally completed in April and May 1986, when Crawley, Faygate, Godstone and Edenbridge mechanical signalboxes were eliminated.

Waterloo Resignalling

The final London resignalling project was announced at the beginning of 1985, when plans were unveiled for a signalling centre at Wimbledon to control Waterloo station and lines to Berrylands, Boxhill, Bookham, Chessington and Putney. The project was christened WARS (Waterloo Area Re-signalling), which after six years in the making and numerous setbacks seemed entirely appropriate. It was the last major relay-based resignalling project before Solid-State Interlocking (SSI) was adopted for all future work at the end of 1985, and consequently by the time Wimbledon Signalling Centre was commissioned, its relay interlocked NX panel was technologically obsolete. Therefore, although chronologically most of the WARS story is outside the parameters of this chapter, it is entirely appropriate to complete the narrative here.

In April 1990, the first stage of the new signalling centre was brought into use and its area of control gradually extended when Clapham Junction A was closed at the end of May, New Malden at the beginning of July and Point Pleasant Junction in September that year.

In September 1990 the existing panel in Waterloo powerbox was moved to a temporary site, so that the 1930s structure could be demolished to make way for the construction of Waterloo International. Finally, over the Easter weekend of 1991, two years after BR's first, and by then state-of-the-art, IECC at Liverpool Street had been brought into use, the electro-mechanically driven NX panel in Wimbledon was fully commissioned.

Below (177):
The impressive interior of the Victoria Signalling Centre, enhanced in this photograph by the use of a wide-angle lens.
The Marconi Co (F81019-01)

SALISBURY WEST

Above (178):
A close-up view of some of the remaining draw-slides in the pneumatic frame at Salisbury West, photographed shortly before closure on 21 August 1981. *BR(S) W11524-5*

Below (179):
GWR 4-6-0 No 7818 *Granville Manor* leaving Southampton with a Cheltenham train on 9 August 1947. *Ian Allan Library*

Southern Region

Outside the London area equally important schemes were completed by the Southern Region at the beginning of the 1980s.

At Salisbury a new panel supplied by Westinghouse was commissioned in August 1981, housed in the station's former parcels room. It took over the work of the two signalboxes fitted with pneumatic frames by the LSWR in 1902 *(Picture 178)* and led to the closure of six other mechanical signalboxes at Dunbridge, Dean, Salisbury Tunnel Junction, Wilton, Wylye and Codford.

The area controlled from Salisbury linked in the east to a new powerbox at Eastleigh, erected behind the 1966 powerbox. In September 1981 the first section of the new NX panel there was brought into use and by the following summer the area of control was extended to Southampton, Romsey, Totton and Fareham, the frequently photographed gantry at the west end of Southampton being a casualty *(Picture 179)*. A feature of the train regulators' panel behind the signalmen's main signalling panel in Eastleigh was the train describer equipment, which took the form of VDUs (visual display units). When the regulator needed to know the exact position of

a particular train, the screens were capable of displaying a section of the track diagram with the particular line occupied by the train highlighted by flashing lights. The equipment could also automatically pass on information about the running of trains to the Train Control Centre at Wimbledon and to the Area Manager's Office in Southampton.

West Hampstead and the 'Leicester Gap' Resignalling

In November 1976 government approval was secured for the £80 million electrification of suburban services out of St Pancras to Bedford. This included resignalling, and to control the route a new powerbox was built at West Hampstead, work starting in the spring of 1977. At the end of that year contracts were signed with Westinghouse for the signalling equipment.

On 15 February 1979 the panel for West Hampstead powerbox was delivered and over the weekend of 20/21 October that year the first section was commissioned, leading to the closure of mechanical signalboxes at Harpenden Station, Harpenden Junction, Luton South and Luton North. One by one the other ex-MR boxes between London and Irchester South, just south of Wellingborough, were closed, until at the beginning of 1982 only the 1957 powerbox at St Pancras remained operational. When this was taken out of use at the beginning of July 1982, the resignalling was complete. Two months later the overhead lines between St Pancras and Bedford were fully energised in readiness for the new electric services.

From the start of the winter timetable 1982, HSTs entered service on the Midland main line and although the southern section had all the trappings of a modern railway, for the next few years there was the incongruous sight of BR's most prestigious trains threading their way through fine arrays of semaphores at Wellingborough, at Leicester and junctions to the south and north of that city *(Picture 180)*. It was not until June 1983

109

Left (182):
The interior of the signalling centre at Leicester before it was fully commissioned.
Zarb Industrial & Commercial Photographers
GRx16

signalling had been improved at the beginning of World War 2 but by the 1980s the steam age track layout had become an operational embarrassment. The solution was to re-lay completely the majority of lines at the station, straighten the through roads, reduce the number of points from 229 to 106 and resignal. To achieve this, Crewe station was closed completely for all but two DMU services to and from Chester and Stafford, between 2 June and 21 July 1985.

Line speed approaching the station was raised from 20 to 50mph, and the main through lines were realigned so that 80mph was possible in place of the previous 25-30mph restrictions. Crewe North and South, equipped with miniature lever frames at the beginning of World War 2, and Crewe A, still retaining its LNWR 'All Electric Crewe' frame of miniature levers, were closed, when their work was taken over by the new Crewe Signalling Centre from 20 July 1985. Two days later the new station was formally opened.

Western Region

On 28 January 1981, the government gave its approval for the £28 million resignalling scheme between Westbury and Totnes. Multi-aspect colour-light signals had been brought into use between Totnes and St Germans on 4/5 May 1974, and the Westbury-Exeter scheme was to be the final link in a continuous chain of colour-light signalling between Paddington and Plymouth. Having drawn attention to the absurdity of British Rail's fastest trains, the HSTs, being signalled through Leicester by semaphores, it must now be said that the sight of the same trains encountering ex-GWR and BR(W) lower quadrant semaphores almost all the way from Westbury, through Taunton, Exeter and Newton Abbot to Totnes, was close to unbelievable and something that only railway enthusiasts could appreciate *(Picture 183)*.

By the end of 1981 the shell of the new powerbox at Westbury had been completed and at the beginning of 1983 the structure at Exeter was in hand. The panels at both places were manufactured and installed by Westinghouse and the first stage at Westbury was commissioned on 14 May 1984. By the beginning of 1985, the work was all but complete and attention turned to Exeter.

Unlike at Westbury and Crewe, Exeter St David's station remained open throughout the remodelling of the track layout. Stage 1 of the project concentrated on the stretch of line from City Basin (Exeter) to Stoke Canon and Stage 2 took colour-light signalling on from Stoke Canon to Tiverton. The rest of the scheme extended through Taunton and Cogload Junction to the east, and through Dawlish and Newton Abbot to Totnes and Paignton in the west.

that final approval was forthcoming for the resignalling of this part of the Midland main line, by then christened the 'Leicester Gap', as it lay between the control areas of Trent and West Hampstead powerboxes.

Construction of the new signalling centre on the site of the former MPD at Leicester began in 1984, and on 29 June 1986 a dozen mechanical signalboxes were closed in the first phase of the resignalling scheme between Syston South Junction (just north of Leicester) and Glendon North, north of Kettering, (exclusive). Phase 2 of the resignalling was completed the following year, when the four remaining mechanical signalboxes north of Leicester were taken out of use in April *(Picture 181)*, and the remaining six between Irchester South and Glendon North were closed on 5/6 December 1987.

The console in Leicester signalling centre was a standard NX one with a large illuminated diagram behind, but what made the Leicester installation important in the history of railway signalling was its claim to be the first to use computer keyboards, 'tracker balls' and VDUs, on which the signalmen could call up train descriptions, signal post telephone circuits and failure indications *(Picture 182)*. The installation was only one step removed from being a fully Integrated Electronic Control Centre (IECC), and helped test the new technology.

Eastern and Anglia Regions

Work started on a replacement for the 1962 powerbox at Colchester at the beginning of 1981 and at the end of the year approval was given for the extension of electrification from there to Norwich. By the spring of the following year, GEC-General Signal had secured the contract to undertake resignalling north of Colchester, through Ipswich to Sproughton and to Westerfield Junction, and in December 1983 the new powerbox was brought into use. Two years later at the end of 1985 the same firm was awarded the contract for resignalling from Norwich to Mellis via Diss and Swainsthorpe.

In the summer of 1981, GEC-General Signal also secured the contract to equip the new powerbox at Cambridge, the structure of which had by then been completed. The area of control would stretch to Royston, Bishop's Stortford, Fulbourne and just south of Ely. The new installation at Cambridge began to control trains in the station area from 17 October 1982 and was formally opened 10 days later by Sir Peter Parker, Chairman of BR. However, all lines were not fully under its control until just before Christmas 1983. Cambridge was one of the first powerboxes to make use of microprocessors, in this case as part of the indicating equipment in the panel. As with other improvement schemes already mentioned, resignalling was justified by, and in this case completed ahead of, electrification. Authorization for this on the lines north of Bishop's Stortford to Cambridge came at the beginning of 1984.

Between 28 and 31 March 1986, Norwich Thorpe station was closed completely to allow track to be relaid and new colour-light signals erected. A new but temporary signalling centre was brought into use on 8 June and remained in use until 15 March the following year, when Norwich came under the control of Colchester powerbox.

Crewe Resignalling

When the electrification of the southern part of the West Coast main line was completed in 1966, a number of pre-nationalisation signalboxes remained. At Crewe the

The first section of the Exeter panel was brought into use in the spring of 1985, when over the weekend of 29 March-1 April Exeter Middle and Cowley Bridge Junction signalboxes were closed, followed by Exeter West (*Picture 184*) and Exeter Central on 6 May, Stoke Canon becoming the temporary fringe box. Work then progressed east towards Taunton, and Silk Mill Crossing, just to the west of the station there, became the next temporary fringe to Exeter panel on the first weekend of March 1986. At the beginning of April that year further closures meant that only Taunton East Junction remained operational between Bristol and Westbury powerboxes and the Exeter panel. Taunton East was finally taken out of use on 21/23 March 1987 and the Exeter panel linked directly with Westbury and Bristol powerboxes.

The final stage of resignalling concentrated on work to the west of Exeter, the mechanical signalboxes at City Basin, Exminster, Dawlish Warren and Teignmouth closing in November 1986, followed by Newton Abbot East and West, Aller Junction and Dainton Tunnel in May 1987. When Totnes closed on 8 November that year, making Plymouth powerbox Exeter's neighbour, the project was complete and the lower quadrant semaphore signal had finally been eliminated from Britain's main lines

Above (183):
The west end of Taunton station on 17 July 1985. *Author*

Below (184):
An Ian Allan *Trains Illustrated* excursion hauled by 'Merchant Navy' No 35023 *Holland-Afrika Line* passing Exeter West signalbox on 20 September 1958. *Derek Herman*

Left (185):
The equipment installed in the new Doncaster North signalbox and brought into use in February 1949 marked a significant stage in the development of route-setting panels. Unfortunately, apart from this and the panels in Doncaster South and Potters Bar, no other fundamental signalling improvements were carried out on the main line between King's Cross and Doncaster until the 1970s.
Fastline Photographic, York (185260)

Below left (186):
No 47408 hauling the up 'Flying Scotsman' on 5 February 1977, approaching Black Carr Junction just south of Doncaster, controlled by standard upper quadrant semaphores fitted by BR onto ex-GNR lattice and wooden signal posts. *G. W. Morrison*

(though it still survives on secondary routes). The GWR had been one of the last railway companies to adopt the lower quadrant semaphore in the 1870s and its successor, the Western Region of British Railways, was the last to abandon its use.

Leamington Spa and the Solid-State Interlocking (SSI) Project

Elsewhere on former GWR territory, another signalling revolution was taking place in the mid-1980s. After experiments by BR signalling engineers, a joint agreement with GEC-General Signal and Westinghouse Signals was entered into in 1981 to develop a microprocessor-based signalling system. The most significant advantages of using this sort of equipment were the lower cost than traditional electro-mechanical relays and the reduction in the size of relay rooms, if not their complete elimination.

Miniaturisation of the relay had reached the point beyond which it could not be developed any further. In the new solid-state system, the 'interlocking logic' as it was called, the proving of signals and points through track circuits etc, was carried out by one or more microcomputers. The information from points, signals, track circuits and the position of trains was all collated and cross-checked before routes were set, either automatically using ARS (mentioned in connection with the Three Bridges resignalling), or by the signalman via a conventional NX panel, or a computer keyboard and VDU.

It was decided to pilot the SSI scheme at Leamington Spa and the contract for building the powerbox there was awarded in the summer of 1983. By the end of 1984 the new equipment had been installed and on 22 January the following year, trials of the hardware were officially started. A traditional NX panel was used, the tests at first being carried out with simulated trains. Gradually, as these tests were completed to the satisfaction of the engineers, the panel and

processors were connected up to lineside signals and points.

By the time these trials were successfully completed and BR had approved the use of SSI in September 1985, plans had already been formulated for other SSI installations. In the spring of 1987 CAP Industry Ltd was awarded a £2 million contract to develop what was christened the Integrated Electronic Control Centre (IECC). Based on microprocessor technology and computer software, it was to be integrated with the Solid-State Interlocking to become the basis of all future resignalling work. The development of the Integrated Electronic Control Centre (IECC) ranks with the perfecting and installation of the electric telegraph in the 1840s and the production of Stevens' and Saxby's interlocking lever frames of 1860, and the following chapter deals exclusively with this impressive technology.

East Coast Main Line

As the previous chapter concluded with a survey of the West Coast resignalling and electrification, so this chapter finishes with a look at the East Coast main line. The contrast between the modernisation of the two could not be greater. Resignalling of the East Coast route was a protracted affair and it was finally achieved over two and a half years before the government gave its approval for electrification. It was also achieved in less than coherent stages. It was ironic that the LNER should have led signalling developments immediately before World War 2 and then its successors, the Eastern and North Eastern Regions, should have lost out to other regions in the hectic modernisation period of the late 1950s and 1960s (*Picture 185*).

But sometimes adversity brings out the best in people, and this appears to have been so with the Eastern Region's management. Despite being starved of investment in the late 1960s and early 1970s and having to control trains in many areas with oil-lit semaphore signals operated from pre-Grouping mechanical signalboxes, the region accelerated its diesel-hauled passenger services to a level where they seriously competed with those on the fully modernised West Coast main line. A few mechanical signalboxes were closed on the ex-GNR section of line, but there was only piecemeal substitution of colour-light signals for semaphores. Nevertheless, track was rationalised and upgraded, and in 1970 a number of stretches were passed for 95-100mph running, resulting in a significant acceleration of expresses between King's Cross and Newcastle.

Ahead of government backing, and characterising the Region's optimistic outlook, the shell of a new powerbox was started at King's Cross in 1969. At the end of 1970 approval was given to spend £7.4 million on resignalling between London and Sandy, but the cost of the project did not include immunisation against inter-ference from any future 25kV overhead

electrification. The government may have seen electrification of the main line as a very distant goal, but surprisingly it announced its approval for limited electrification, ie for suburban services between King's Cross and Moorgate to Royston via Hitchin and Hertford North, only a year later on 18 August 1971.

At the beginning of the following year, approval was gained for the remodelling of tracks through Peterborough station, a number of abortive plans for which had been tabled since the 1930s. The layout was so bad that for more than a century, all trains had been slowed to no more than 20mph through the station. The approval also covered the provision of a new powerbox. Progress was rapid, and the first stage of this was commissioned on 3 December 1972. By the beginning of the new May 1973 timetable the new layout was complete and main line trains were able to pass through Peterborough at 100mph. A few more precious minutes had been cut off the journey time between London and Scotland. Just a year before full electrification of the West Coast main line to Glasgow, the East Coast was once again showing what diesel haulage could achieve.

1974 proved to be a good year for both regions. As O. S. Nock marvelled at the changes to services over Shap and Beattock, GEC-General Signal was securing the £1.2 million contract to supply the multi-aspect signals between Sandy and Holme and between Helpston and Stoke Tunnel, extending the Peterborough control area. In the same year, authority was finally won for the new powerbox at Doncaster, to complete the resignalling of the East Coast main line between London and York. The contract for this work was awarded to Westinghouse in the summer of the following year, with completion scheduled for 1978.

There was then a lull in activities, and it was not until November 1976 that new electric trains began running between Moorgate and Welwyn Garden City and Hertford North. But before these services were extended into King's Cross, the track layout at the station's throat had to be simplified. Work on this started in January 1977 and finally in April that year the King's Cross powerbox was fully commissioned. The new panel controlled 83½ route and 260 track miles, and was capable of setting 980 routes. It not only superseded the 1932 signalbox at the terminus with its 232-miniature lever frame (closed early in March 1977), but a further 56 mechanical signalboxes with a total of 2,561 levers, as well as the 1959 panel box at Potters Bar (closed 25 March 1973). Overhead wires were then run into the terminus, and from 3 October 1977 the first suburban electric services started running out to Hitchin and Royston, followed in February 1978 by a full service.

By then, all the ex-GNR and ex-LNER mechanical signalboxes between King's Cross and Hitchin had closed and the majority northwards to Doncaster had also been eliminated. However, a number were stripped of their frames and equipped with NX panels and closed-circuit televisions to monitor adjacent crossings, while at other strategic

locations, mainly at level crossings, new boxes were erected with the same equipment. Until Doncaster powerbox was complete, these structures had the status of signalboxes, actively controlling the passage of trains (Pictures 186 & 187).

The last semaphore disappeared from the East Coast main line on 27 September 1978, when the up home at Decoy No 2, just south of Doncaster, was removed, and in the summer of 1979 the first section of the panel in Doncaster powerbox was commissioned to control the station area. Further stages followed until completion was achieved at the end of 1981, Sir Peter Parker, Chairman of BR, officially declaring it open on 8 December 1981 (Picture 188). By then, 70 mechanical signalboxes had closed and the panel signalboxes mentioned above had been downgraded to gateboxes.

Three years behind schedule, the statistics for Doncaster were still impressive. It controlled the main line from just south of Grantham, where it linked with the Peterborough powerbox, northwards to the point where the Selby diversion (not used by passenger trains until 1983) left the original alignment controlled from a panel in the 1951 York signalbox. Doncaster was, of course, also a major freight junction for both the South Yorkshire and North Nottinghamshire coalfields, so most of the possible 1,164 routes available over 160 route and 380 track miles were for this traffic. Flashing double yellow and/or single yellow indications were installed at four high speed junctions, three

being on the approach to Doncaster itself. Fifteen hot-box detectors were provided within the panel area, close to locations where offending vehicles could be removed from trains.

At Newark, plans to build a flyover for the Nottingham-Lincoln line had been abandoned long before the completion of the resignalling, so the double line flat crossing remained. Track circuiting for all four lines there was impossible, so circuits were arranged for only the main East Coast route, while axle counters checked the passage of trains running over the crossing on the Nottingham-Lincoln line.

The commissioning of Doncaster powerbox completed the resignalling of the main line between King's Cross and York, just in time for the introduction of the Eastern Region's HST fleet. This, as with resignalling, turned out to be a protracted affair, with the first production HST running from 20 March 1978, followed progressively by others until HSTs dominated the timetable at the beginning of the 1980s. Nevertheless, as on the Western Region, their use immediately boosted passenger numbers and income ahead of full electrification.

Resignalling at the northern reaches of the East Coast main line had started in the summer of 1974. The project was christened the Edinburgh & East of Scotland Resignalling and covered the 243 route miles between Berwick and Cupar on the East Coast main line, to Polmont on the Glasgow line, to Ladybank and Hilton Junction (Perth), and to Midcalder. It was to be controlled from a new

signalling centre at Edinburgh Waverley. The £5.4 million contract to provide the new equipment at Edinburgh was awarded to GEC-General Signal in February 1976. Work advanced well and on 3 October that year the first stage was commissioned and colour-light signalling was brought into use between Edinburgh and Berwick in March 1978. The contract to extend the colour-light signal area further over the Forth Bridge — Stage 6 — was signed on 29 June 1979 and by November 1981, the Edinburgh & East of Scotland resignalling scheme was complete. Sixty-six mechanical signalboxes had been eliminated as a result.

To complete the story, a considerably smaller scheme based on Aberdeen's new signalling centre at Clayhills was also brought into use during 1981, controlling just 17 route miles from Dyce through Aberdeen to Newtonhill.

Perhaps not accorded the same accolades as the modernisation of the West Coast main line in 1966 and again eight years later, the upgrading of services over the East Coast route was undoubtedly a considerable achievement, and one which obviously helped the Region's management in its lobbying for electrification capital. Its campaigning finally paid off when, on 27 July 1984, the government announced its financial backing for the £305 million project to electrify the East Coast main line northwards from Hitchin to Leeds and Edinburgh. It was the largest and the last direct government-funded project for a state-owned British Railways.

Above left (187):
The interior of the ex-GNR signalbox at Bridge Junction, Doncaster, during its final weeks. The block shelf supported a mixture of GNR, LNER and BR equipment (the three large cabinets in the centre were the train describers working to the 1949 Doncaster South signalling panel). Photographed on 3 July 1979, the box finally closed on 8 September 1979.
Fastline Photographic, York (797.3276.6)

Above (188):
The Decoy section of the Doncaster NX panel. The tracks around Bridge Junction are just obscured by the signalman's left arm. *BR(E)*

Right (188a):
This photograph illustrates all too well how long overdue was the resignalling of the former GNR section of the East Coast main line by the 1970s. The signalbox at Tuxford (North) was over 100 years old when this photograph was taken on 14 October 1975 to commemorate the opening of the new road bridge in the background which replaced the level crossing. The signalbox itself finally closed on 2 May 1976. *Newark Advertiser*

With British Rail on the threshold of a new era in signalling, the Clapham accident at the end of 1988 was a terrible reminder that safety cannot be taken for granted and that no matter how sophisticated the technology, human error can defeat any system.

On the morning of 12 December 1988 a Basingstoke-Waterloo train standing at a signal between Earlsfield and Clapham Junction was run into by a Bournemouth-Waterloo train. The wreckage was then hit by an empty stock train travelling in the opposite direction. Thirty-four people were killed and 100 injured. The accident was due to a signal failure, eventually traced back to a redundant piece of wire in Clapham Junction A signalbox, which during resignalling there in connection with the Wimbledon/Waterloo scheme had not been properly terminated. Signalboxes all over the country contained such redundant wires, which had caused no problems, but when the report on the accident was published in November 1989, among its 93 recommendations were tighter procedures for planning, supervising and checking new signalling installations. This inevitably delayed many signalling projects up and down the country, a problem compounded in the first few years of the 1990s by uncertainty as to what privatisation would bring.

On 5 November 1993 the Privatisation Act received the Royal Assent, and five months later on 1 April 1994 British Rail was broken up into component parts. The infrastructure, track, bridges, etc and signalling became the responsibility of Railtrack; in essence, BR without the trains. It is somewhat ironic that on the eve of privatisation, a national timetable played a key role in the operation of the very latest signalling technology. This technology took BR perhaps the closest it ever came to fulfilling the 1948 vision of a co-ordinated railway network. This chapter starts with that new technology and ends with privatisation.

Above left (189):
The south workstation of the York IECC, photographed on 10 March 1997. *Author*

Left (190):
The replacement multi-lens colour-light signal (with the cross) in place behind the twin-lens searchlight signal and route indicator, which had been brought into use with Northallerton signalbox on 3 September 1939 (seen in the background). The photograph was taken on 13 April 1990, two days before the closure of Northallerton signalbox. *Ian S. Carr*

The Integrated Electronic Control Centre (IECC)

The achievement of the late 1980s and early 1990s was undoubtedly the Integrated Electronic Control Centre (IECC). It was a fundamental change compared with what had gone before, the contrast as marked as that between steam and electric traction or between semaphores and colour-light signals. At the lineside nothing appeared to have changed, the colour-light signals were still multi-lens, multi-aspect. But for the signalmen, or 'signallers' as they soon became, their working environment was totally transformed. Not only was the IECC a technological achievement, but, despite the consequences of the Clapham accident and the lead-up to privatisation, the speed at which it was put into active use was also very impressive. The first three installations were up and running by the summer of 1989, barely two years after development work had started. By the summer of 1994 the total had risen to 10. As the IECC was the dominant force in resignalling in the years immediately before privatisation, older technology will be mentioned only in passing in this chapter.

The IECC brought together Automatic Route Setting (ARS) first tried out at Three Bridges in 1983, Solid-State Interlocking (SSI) tried and tested at Leamington Spa in 1985, and standard computer hardware (keyboard, VDU and tracker ball) trialled at Leicester in 1987. In an IECC installation, the most obvious difference compared with previous signalling centres was the complete absence of the illuminated diagram. Its function was transferred to a number of VDUs capable of displaying selected sections of track. Depending on the complexity of the area, an IECC was provided with a number of signalmen's 'workstations' equipped with VDUs, keyboards and tracker balls. In the standard installation there were three VDUs dedicated to displaying the track layout per workstation, two normally showing the whole area under the control of the signalman, while the other displayed a specific area in more detail. As with an illuminated diagram, signals, points, track circuits and train descriptions were all shown. Normally, routes would be set automatically by the computer (ARS) from the National Timetable Processor, the system being able to deal with trains running up to one hour early or three hours late. Outside these times or in emergencies, the signalman could set the route by rotating the tracker ball until the cursor on the VDU displaying a detailed area

was next to the appropriate menu command or signal icon. He then pressed the entrance and exit buttons next to the ball. Points could be altered in the same way and they, and routes, could also be altered by using the keyboard instead of the tracker ball. Any direct action by the signalman was displayed on the VDUs in a colour different from that shown if actions had been taken automatically.

The IECCs' ability to take information from the National Timetable Processor and automatically organise train routes, while at the same time feeding the actual running of trains back to management, station staff and into passenger information systems, made them a great advance on their signalling centre predecessors. From a historical perspective, IECCs could be said to have descended more from the pioneering train control systems of the early 20th century than from the humble signalbox. It is, however, a matter of conjecture as to whether IECC could have coped with the amount and type of traffic that those early staff-intensive train control systems were set up to monitor and try to regulate. But perhaps that is an unfair comparison which should not detract from the revolutionary character of the IECC.

1989

Liverpool Street

The first IECC was commissioned at Liverpool Street station, London, in 1989. The rebuilding of Liverpool Street had started in the late 1980s during the capital's redevelopment boom and it was officially opened by HM The Queen on 5 December 1991. The station was closed completely over the Easter period in 1989 for track remodelling and for new colour-light signals to be installed, after which the new IECC was switched on on 24 March, working to Bow and Hackney Downs powerboxes. The 1949 Liverpool Street powerbox, along with Bethnal Green, closed at the same time. Unfortunately, there were considerable teething problems with the new signalling, attributed to interference from the high voltage traction currents, and *Railway Magazine* for June 1989 could not resist printing the headline 'High-tech signalling brings Liverpool Street to standstill'.

The ultimate aim of the project was to control the former GE main line from just two signalling centres at Liverpool Street and Colchester, and as part of this strategy the area of Liverpool Street's control was gradually extended. At the beginning of 1994 the rationalisation of the tangle of tracks at Stratford started, just after the LNER signalboxes at Romford and Gidea Park and

Left (191):
The 1960 powerbox at Dumbarton, photographed on 15 August 1960 when new. *BR(Sc)*

Below left (192):
The former GCR mechanical signalbox at Sudbury Hill closed on 29 May 1990, when a further section of the Marylebone IECC was brought into use. *Robert Humm Collection*

stage was brought into use when five signalboxes closed, including the 1960 powerbox at Hyndland. Over the next few years more boxes were abolished as the area of control was extended, the project being completed when Bowling, Craigendoran and the Dumbarton powerbox of 1960 succumbed in February 1992 *(Picture 191)*.

1990-1992

Marylebone

The fourth IECC to be commissioned was at Marylebone station, London. As with so much of railway history, there was a touch of irony in this story.

Since the former GCR main line had closed north of Aylesbury in 1966, the remaining lines into Marylebone had not been modernised, and as a result this London terminus was the very last controlled by semaphore signals. It appeared that traditional mechanical signalling would see the Victorian terminus through to the end, as semaphores were still there in 1984 when the decision to close the station was announced. Two years later, however, in the summer of 1986 the threat was lifted and with a commitment to improve services came plans to resignal the line between Marylebone, High Wycombe, Princes Risborough and Aynho Junction, just south of Banbury, and through Amersham to Aylesbury, including the connection between the latter and Princes Risborough, a total of 88 route miles. The irony was that the signalling would be controlled from a new IECC, and this immediately meant that Marylebone, from having the oldest signalling installation, would have the most modern train control system of any London terminus apart from Liverpool Street.

The first stage of the new IECC was commissioned on 22 April 1990 *(Picture 192)* and completed in the first week of March 1991, when High Wycombe (South) and Princes Risborough (North) mechanical signalboxes were closed.

Tyneside

Once the track remodelling and resignalling at York was complete, work advanced northwards along the East Coast main line between Danby Wiske, just south of Darlington, through Newcastle to Morpeth. At Newcastle track layouts were extensively rationalised, the famous and often photographed series of diamond crossings to

the 1949 powerboxes at Ilford, Ilford Car Sheds, Bow Junction, Forest Gate and Goodmayes were taken out of use.

York

The second IECC was brought into use at York, barely two months after the installation at Liverpool Street. Approval for this £18 million project had been secured at the end of 1986 and work started in February 1988 as part of the East Coast main line electrification.

As with all modern resignalling projects, there was a major rationalisation of track and simplification of layouts, particularly on the approaches to York station. The north end was tackled between September and November 1988, followed by the south end between February and June 1989. During this phase the first stage of the IECC was commissioned over the weekend of 11-14 May, during which time the impressive

OCS panel of 1951 was taken out of use. Full commissioning was achieved on 10 September 1989 and then attention turned to lines north of York *(Picture 189)*. Tollerton and Thirsk signalboxes closed in December 1989 and January 1990 respectively, followed by the closure of Northallerton on 15 April 1990 *(Picture 190)*. At this date the York scheme was complete but work was already in hand on Tyneside, where the East Coast main line's next IECC was to be located.

Yoker

As this chapter is looking at the spread of the IECC in chronological order, two others had opened before Tyneside was operational. The first of these was commissioned north of the border at Yoker, a few miles to the west of Glasgow, during July 1989. The contract for the design and installation of the Yoker equipment had been won by GEC-General Signal at the beginning of 1987, and the first

Above (193):
The Westinghouse 'L' 155-miniature lever frame, brought into use in Darlington South signalbox on 6 May 1939 and taken out of use almost exactly 52 years later on 10 May 1991, during the final stages of the commissioning of the Tyneside IECC. *Modern Transport*

the east of the station being replaced by simple turnouts.

The IECC was built south of the Tyne and equipped with three workstations, controlling the Newcastle area, the Gateshead/Heworth area and the Darlington area. The Gateshead workstation was commissioned on 12-15 April 1991, followed by the Newcastle one on 19-22 April and finally the Darlington one on 9-18 May 1991 *(Picture 193)*.

The resignalling led to the closure of not only the 1959 Newcastle panel and the LNER signalbox at Darlington, but the 'modernisation' powerboxes at Benton, Gateshead, Tyne Yard and Heaton. Interestingly, it was thought impracticable to put all the closed-circuit TV screens monitoring road level crossings into Tyneside, so signalboxes at Morpeth, Alnmouth and Tweedmouth were retained. The latter 1960s powerbox received new solid-state interlocking in July 1991 when the other 'modernisation' box at Benton was closed.

With the completion of resignalling at Newcastle, the East Coast main line between London and the Scottish capital — 393½ route miles — was controlled from just nine signalling centres at King's Cross, Peterborough, Doncaster, York, Tyneside, Morpeth, Alnmouth, Tweedmouth and Edinburgh. Most of the line between York and Edinburgh was also signalled for bi-directional running. Trains working 'wrong line' were limited to 70mph, the track circuits operating warble alarms to warn those working by the lineside of their approach.

Slough

There were many reasons for resignalling Paddington and its approaches, but two of the most important were the replacement of relay interlocking with SSI to achieve full immunisation for Channel Tunnel trains using North Pole Depot and any future electrified service out of Paddington, and secondly to enable track to be relaid so that high speeds could be achieved sooner by trains departing from the terminus.

The resignalling included the construction of an IECC at Slough to take over the work of the 1967 Old Oak Common powerbox. Work on this project started at the end of 1991 and the first stage of the IECC was brought into use just after Christmas 1992, its area of control progressively enlarged so that Old Oak Common powerbox was finally taken out of use on 30 May 1995.

1993 and 1994
Ashford

Westinghouse was awarded the contract to resignal the line between Chislehurst and Orpington, Sevenoaks, Tonbridge, Ashford and Folkestone in November 1989, in preparation for the running of Channel Tunnel trains. This was the cost-saving and short-term alternative to the building of a dedicated new line for London-Paris services. To control the area a new IECC was planned for Ashford with 18 SSIs. Between Sevenoaks and the entrance to the Channel Tunnel, the line was resignalled for bi-directional running and the line speed was increased to 100mph, a very modest achievement when compared with the 300km/h (187.5mph) which Eurostar could reach on France's purpose-built high speed line. By the end of 1993 the project was all but complete, the 'modernisation' powerboxes at Tonbridge, Orpington, Chislehurst Junction and Sevenoaks having closed. The 1962 powerbox at Ashford was finally decommissioned on 12 December 1995.

Sandhills

The creation of an IECC to control the lines centred on Liverpool run by Merseyrail was part of that Passenger Transport Executive's

initiative to improve rail services between the city, Birkenhead, West Kirby and New Brighton to the west, and between Liverpool, Kirkby, Ormskirk, Southport and Burscough Bridge to the north. Expenditure of over £20 million on the scheme was approved by Merseyrail in June 1989. The area covered by the project was one of the last in the country still heavily reliant on mechanical signalboxes and semaphore signals. By the time the scheme was completed in February 1994 and the new IECC at Sandhills, just north of the city centre, had been commissioned, 26 traditional signalboxes had been abolished, as well as the powerbox at Southport with its miniature lever frame opened by the L&YR in 1917.

Upminster

The Upminster IECC (*Pictures 194 & 195*) opened in September 1994, five months after privatisation, and, strictly speaking, should not be in this chapter. However, as authority for the £50 million resignalling of the former LTSR had been secured at the end of 1991, it can still be termed a British Railways project and is included here to end this narrative. The LNER overhead signalbox at Fenchurch Street closed on 22 July 1994, and by the time the whole project was complete in May 1996, all 15 signalboxes along the former LTSR, either built or modernised at the beginning of the 1960s, had been abolished, including the powerboxes at Southend Central and Pitsea opened in 1960, and at Barking, Tilbury Riverside and Ripple Lane opened in 1961 (see Chapter 5).

Above (194):
Contrary to recent trends, the IECC at Upminster is a pleasing structure with some architectural merit.
Fastline Photographic, York (9410 3367.1)

Below (195):
The main workstation of the Upminster IECC, photographed on 12 October 1994.
Fastline Photographic, York (9410 3367.21)

8 Single Lines

As already mentioned in Chapter 1, the benefits of controlling trains on single lines using the electric telegraph was advocated in Cooke's *Telegraphic Railways* of 1842. By the 1860s, with very few exceptions, single lines were protected by the telegraph, not as he envisaged, but using single-needle instruments at each end of individual sections. In the 1870s Tyer & Co was marketing a modified version of its one-wire, two-position instrument especially for use on single lines but in essence it was no better or worse than installing a three-wire, three-position electric telegraph circuit with a single needle and single-stroke bell, as used on the majority of ordinary double lines.

The Board of Trade was certainly not convinced of the safety of employing only an ordinary single-needle instrument or one of Tyer's type, and it was very keen to encourage railway companies to make trains passing through a single line carry with them some unique item signifying authority to be in that section — a token of authority. At first this token was either a person — a pilotman — or a wooden staff. Obviously, this only worked if trains ran alternately from either end of the section. If more than one train needed to pass in any one direction, the pilotman and/or the staff had to make a non-revenue-earning journey back to the other end of the section before the second train could proceed.

This problem was neatly solved by attaching a key to the end of the staff, which could be used to unlock a box containing paper tickets. When a ticket was signed by the signalman (and pilotman), a train could be dispatched without the staff. Once at the other end of the section, the ticket was given up, the signalman there telegraphed to say the train had arrived, and a second train could be dispatched with either the staff or another ticket *(Picture 196)*. The disadvantage of the system was that it relied completely on the conscientiousness of the signalmen regulating it. It depended on one of the signalmen not dispatching another train into the section with a ticket before the first train had arrived, and it relied on the other signalman confirming by telegraph that the correct ticket had been given up by the correct train.

What finally led to a significant development in single line control methods was a serious head-on collision between Thorpe and Brundall on the GER in September 1874, which caused public outrage. Following this accident, Edward Tyer set out to design a system which combined both the physical security of staff working and the communication possible with the electric telegraph. What he finally patented in 1878 were two electro-mechanical instruments. A pair of instruments were installed at either end of a single line section. When a train was to be dispatched, a plunger on the instrument was pressed to sound the bell at the other end of the section. When the appropriate bell codes were exchanged between the signalmen or station staff responsible for working the equipment, the man at the end of the section to which the train was to travel held down his plunger. This lifted the lock in the instrument at the opposite end containing a number of circular

Below (196):
The 1860s signalbox and double arm station semaphore at Much Wenlock station on the GWR's single line branch, photographed before the 1889 Regulation of Railways Act compelled the company to build a fully interlocked signalbox opposite the one shown here and erect new signals. Staff and ticket and telegraph working was replaced by Webb & Thompson electric train staff, which remained in use until the line closed in the 1960s. *Historical Model Railway Society Photograph Collection K15*

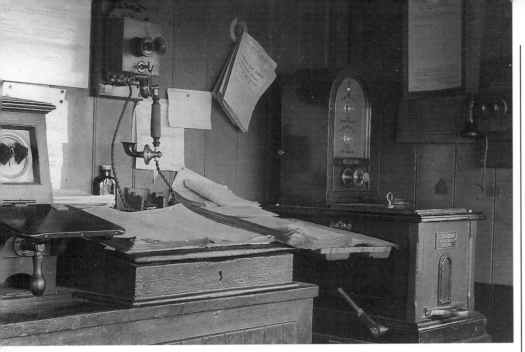

'tablets' — the equivalent of the staff — and allowed the man there to remove one. This then became the authority — the token — for the train driver to travel through the section. Once a tablet had been released, no other could be extracted from the issuing instruments at either end of the section. When the train reached the other station, the tablet was taken and placed into the receiving instrument, this action allowing another tablet to be issued from either end of the section. Tyer's system was immediately superior to staff and ticket working, as every driver was always issued with a tablet, no matter how many trains were travelling in the same direction, whereas the ticket was always a substitute for the actual staff.

Originally tablets for trains travelling in opposite directions along the same section of single line were slightly different, but as only one tablet could be extracted at a time for trains travelling in either direction, Tyer soon modified his system so that tablets were the same for individual sections and only different for adjacent sections. This also meant the issuing and receiving instruments could be combined. The position of notches on the sides of the tablets distinguished which section they applied to.

Tyer & Co continued to improve the design of instrument until by the turn of the century the firm had reached model No 8 (*Pictures 197 & 198*). Surprisingly the Board of Trade was not convinced about the use of Tyer's equipment and still favoured the staff & ticket system supplemented by the electric telegraph. It is difficult to understand why this should have been so. Certain railway companies also remained faithful to the old system. One such company was the LNWR, which eventually went to the trouble of designing its own electric train staff instrument. In 1889 F. W. Webb and A. M. Thompson took out a patent (No 1263) for their new equipment and licensed its manufacture to the Railway Signal Co, which was then able to supply it to other companies. As with Tyer's tablet system, the principle was that instruments worked in pairs and once one staff had been extracted, another could not be obtained from either one of the pair until the first had been returned to one of them. So that staffs could not be inadvertently returned to an instrument controlling another section, the disposition of rings along the body of the staffs varied. Some staffs were also made with keys built into the end, so that ground frames operating intermediate sidings on single lines could be locked and unlocked.

Although the overall design of Webb & Thompson's equipment remained unchanged, various modifications were made over the years. Instruments were made which could hold twice as many staffs, and after it was discovered that it was possible to extract more than one staff at a time if enough force was applied to the release mechanism, this was altered (*Picture 199*). The final refinement was the manufacture of a miniature version of the equipment, the staffs being reduced in size from just under 2ft long to 10¾in.

Until the Grouping of 1923 and for many years afterwards, Tyer's tablet and Webb & Thompson's electric staff systems remained the most common form of single line control. Both systems remained in use until the 1960s but by then they had been largely superseded by 'key token' working. This had been patented in 1912 (No 23417) by A. T. Blackall, the Signal Engineer of the GWR, and his assistant C. M. Jacobs. The Marlow branch was the first to receive the new equipment at the beginning of 1914, and Tyer & Co was granted the licence to manufacture and market it. The instrument became No 9 in the firm's range of single line equipment (*Picture 200*).

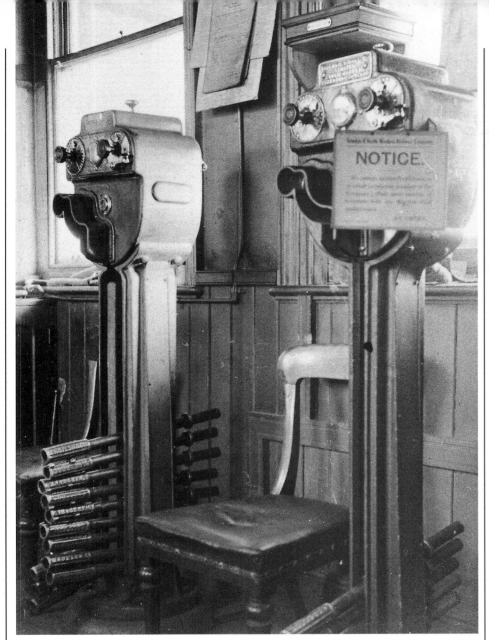

Exchange Equipment

Almost all single line token instruments were located at stations where there might be two tracks, so that trains running in opposite directions could cross. Not all trains stopped at every station, however, and at many locations the exchange of tokens was done while the train was still in motion. Speeds had to be kept very low so that the fireman and signalman did not fail to collect the token or, worse still, injure themselves in the process. Tablets could be put into leather pouches attached to metal hoops, which made catching and dispatching easier *(Picture 201)*. Similar hoops were attached to staffs, but it was really only safe for firemen to collect them while on the move. It became dangerous for signalman to attempt to catch them from a moving locomotive with all the stored momentum involved.

At the very end of the 19th century a number of apparatuses for catching and dispatching tablets and staffs safely at speed were brought into use. The simplest arrangement for dealing with staffs, used by the GWR and other companies, took the form of two posts approximately 60ft apart. On one was attached a metal arm with either padding or a net behind it, the fireman slipping the hoop attached to the staff over the arm as the locomotive passed. On the other post, the staff attached to its hoop could be positioned by the signalman at about 60° to the horizontal, just high enough above the track so that the fireman could put his arm through the hoop, his shoulder and back cushioning the impact. On the M&GN a similar arrangement was used for catching tablets in their leather pouches attached to a metal hoop, although they were still handed by the signalman to the fireman.

By the beginning of the 20th century equipment had been devised to enable tablets to be exchanged automatically while the locomotive was moving at speed (up to 60mph) without the need for a fireman to aim at a post or the signalman at the arm of a fireman. Eliminating the human limb from the exchange process reduced the risk of injury, increased the frequency of trains and consequently enabled passenger services to be improved enormously.

The earliest of these devices was brought into use on the Great North of Scotland Railway in May 1889. It was designed by the company's Locomotive Superintendent James Manson and by the turn of the century was used on the single lines of the neighbouring Highland and Caledonian railways. The tablets were placed in leather pouches with metal reinforcements top and bottom. The pouch to be given up either from the locomotive or the signalbox was pushed into a spring clip or fork, the top metal reinforcement preventing it from falling out of the clip. The lineside equipment consisted of a cast-iron post 5ft 4½in from track level, on top of which was mounted a retractable metal arm. At its end was the fork for dispatching the pouch and a pair of jaws for catching the pouch from the locomotive. In the dispatching position the pouch was parallel with the track. A matching pair of jaws and clip were attached to an arm to the left-hand side of the locomotive. Once tablets had been exchanged, the arm on the engine could be raised against the cabside and the pouch and tablet brought into the cab.

It was not until the beginning of the 20th century that automatic exchange equipment was used on an English line. This was designed and patented (1905, No 861) by

A. Whitaker, the Locomotive Superintendent of the Somerset & Dorset Railway. Whitaker's device used pouches with miniature hoops attached. There were two forms of the catching device but both had metal jaws similar to Manson's equipment, positioned at the end of a movable metal arm. At passing places on a single line, where tablets were exchanged, the arm was horizontal and positioned just above another arm, on which the tablet to be taken by the locomotive was fixed. Both arms were attached to a vertical cast-iron post. The arms and jaw were swung out at 90° to the track to dispatch one tablet and catch another, the momentum of that catch swinging the arm and jaw parallel to the track, where a spring clip held it in that position (Picture 202).

The second form of the mechanism only caught tablets and was used where the single line became a double track section. In the catching position, the arm was vertical with the jaw at the top, the momentum of catching the tablet throwing the arm backwards so that the jaw ended up at rail level (Picture 203).

Compared to the position of the pouch on the Scottish railways, Whitaker's equipment held them at 90° to the track ready for catching and dispatching. Another difference was that Whitaker fixed the locomotive equipment to the tender not the cab side. The metal jaw for catching the tablet was similar but the tablet to be surrendered by the train was attached to the back of the jaw with its hoop uppermost. During the exchange the jaw was held rigid on an extending arm, only being retracted by the fireman after the exchange. Manson's and Whitaker's exchange equipment remained in use until the end of steam in the late 1960s.

Above Left (201):
The DMU (diesel multiple-unit) driver holds out his arm, while the signalman at Barnstaple Town signalbox aims the hoop attached to the leather pouch containing the single line tablet. *M. S. Dutnie*

Left (202):
A posed photograph of Whitaker's exchange equipment, showing the moment when the jaws at the end of the extended arm on the locomotive's tender snapped around the miniature hoop attached to the leather pouch which was clipped onto the curved arm of the lineside apparatus, while at the same time the leather pouch clipped onto the back of the jaws on the tender arm was picked up by the jaws attached to the top arm of the lineside equipment. *Ian Allan Library*

Above (203):
Templecombe Junction on the former S&DJ photographed on 18 March 1952. The large fabricated metal object between the left-hand track and the line on which 4-4-0 No 40509 is approaching is the second form of Whitaker's catching device. The arm cannot be seen because it is at 45° to the ground with the jaws at ballast level. No 40509 is about to collect the token inside the leather pouch attached to a variant of the catching device just described. As the jaws on the tender snap up the pouch, the force will push the arm of the lineside equipment down to ballast level. *S. C. Townroe*

Centralised Traffic Control (CTC)

This was one of the children of the 1955 Modernisation Programme that did not reach maturity. In the history of signalling, it was a planned revolution that did not happen but faded quietly away during the mid-1960s and has not been heard of since. The terminology had been coined in the USA, where a postwar programme of track circuiting single lines and installing remotely operated motor points, worked from a few strategically positioned control centres, had significantly improved working practices. The technology required for CTC was not particularly revolutionary, it was only the greater distances involved that caught the imagination of contemporary writers. For example, in a *Trains Illustrated* article for March 1955 the author commented that, '…it is an eerie experience to see the exit points from a crossing loop move and the signal light change, and then realise that they do so in response to the flick of a switch 50, 75, maybe 100 miles away'.

But in the end the reasons for implementing CTC in this country were flawed. The aim was to reduce the costs of operating single lines by removing all the intermediate signalboxes, attendant operating and maintenance staff. But the capital costs of full track circuiting and cabling to distant point motors to achieve the revenue savings were just too high to be justified. When Perth powerbox was designed in 1958, it incorporated a space for a CTC control panel for the line to Inverness, but by the time the box opened in 1962, the CTC idea had been abandoned, described in a *Modern Railways* article as '…an unjustifiable luxury'.

In Wales, CTC was planned to transform the Central Wales line, but in the end it drove it to the brink of closure. At the end of 1956, S. G. Hearn, Chief Operating Superintendent of the Western Region, disclosed in his paper 'The Outlook on Modern Railway Operation', delivered to the Institute of Transport, that consideration was being given to the introduction of CTC on the Central Wales line from Craven Arms to Swansea. He said that its use would double the freight capacity of the line. Authorization for CTC between Craven Arms and Llandovery, with a new central powerbox at Llandrindod Wells, continuous track circuiting and new lifting barriers at certain level crossings, followed in the spring of 1960. Eighteen mechanical signalboxes were to be closed, key token working abolished and many sections of double track reduced to single line. The scheme was costed at £676,000. By modernising this route it was hoped to divert steel and coal traffic from West Wales to the Midlands and elsewhere. The new Llanwern Steelworks was due to open in 1961 and the signalling around Newport was due to be improved as well.

But the optimism was completely misplaced, the scheme never materialised and to reduce costs, the traditional post-Beecham formula was applied. In 1965 through freights were withdrawn and line capacity was considerably reduced when most signalboxes closed, key token working was abandoned and staff and ticket working introduced, with signalmen communicating by GPO telephones. The line struggled on in this form with the remaining fully staffed stations and signalboxes for another 20 years, before the Provincial Sector of BR decided to invest in equipping it with 'No Signalman key token' working in 1985 — see below.

Tokenless Block

After BR had abandoned CTC, it turned first to 'tokenless block' working. As the terminology implies, the only thing missing from this system was the token. Otherwise, the method of operation was very similar to traditional single line working. Two different systems emerged in the 1960s, used on the Scottish and the Western Regions.

In Scotland the special instrument mounted on the block shelf took the form of a large metal box containing the relevant relays *(Picture 204)*. After exchanging bell codes, the signalman giving permission for a train to approach turned an acceptance switch on his instrument. The signalman receiving that acceptance then pressed his instrument plunger until the indication 'train going to' was displayed, after which the signalman giving the permission pressed his plunger until 'train coming from' was displayed on his instrument. During the pressing of the plungers, the electrical circuitry running through the appropriate relays, lever locks and track circuits proved that a release could be given. At each crossing place, entry and exit track circuits were provided. Once the

train had cleared the exit track circuit (and a treadle) and was travelling through the single line section, the indications on the instruments at both ends of the section could not be altered, the starting signals were locked at danger and consequently no other train could enter the occupied section. A train had to clear the entry track circuit before the signalman could send the 'train out of section' bell code and turn his switch from acceptance to normal. The usual cancelling facilities were provided.

On the Western Region, the special instrument was considerably smaller (as it did not contain the electrical relays) and was built into the same size wooden case as the Region's standard permissive block instrument, which itself was developed out of the GWR new standard absolute block instrument of 1947 *(Picture 205)*. The first line to be protected by the new instruments was the former LSWR main line between Salisbury and Exeter, singled in 1966 between Wilton and Pinhoe with a number of passing loops. In the Western Region's system, no bell codes were exchanged, although signalmen could converse on the

telephone. If a signalman wanted to send a train forward into a single line section, he did not seek permission in the accepted railway sense, but pressed the 'offer' button on his instrument. If the switch on his instrument was at normal and that on the receiving instrument at the other end of the section was in its 'accept' position, if no other trains were in the section and the track circuits were clear, the three-position needle on both instruments would move to 'train accepted'. This released the starting signal lever lock and the train could be signalled into the section. Once in the section, the needle on both instruments automatically dropped to the 'train in section' indication (also the fail-safe position if a fault occurred). When the train arrived at the other end, and had cleared the track circuit ahead of the home signal and the treadle, the signalman there could turn his switch to normal again and press the 'train arrived' button. If the circuitry could prove that all conditions had been met, the needles would swing back to the normal indication. Before another train could be accepted from the same direction (in rear), the first train had to have passed the clearing point/overlap beyond the starting signal.

On the Wilton-Pinhoe section, a number of sidings remained. The points for these were operated from ground frames fitted with Annett's keys, released after a train had occupied a track circuit in rear of the facing points for a set time. Once the train was inside the siding and the Annett's key had been returned to the frame, a plunger located at the siding was pressed, which caused the single line instruments at either end of the section to show normal, thus freeing them for the acceptance of another train. To release the train from the siding, both signalmen had

Left (204):
The Scottish Region tokenless block instrument. *Ian Allan Library*

Above (205):
The Western Region tokenless block instrument. *Ian Allan Library*

to place their instrument switches to 'accept'. An offer plunger at the siding could then be pressed to obtain the Annett's key, so that the ground frame levers could be unlocked. As soon as the train occupied the main line, the instrument indications moved automatically to 'train in section'.

No Signalman Key Token

In essence this was 'do-it-yourself' token working. On the Central Wales line, all the remaining four signalboxes were closed during 1986, only the signalbox at Pantyffynnon being retained to control the line to Craven Arms. Train drivers contacted the signalman at Pantyffynnon by telephone to request a token. If permission was given, the driver withdrew a token from the instrument located in a locked cupboard at each crossing place. Points at crossing places were arranged so they normally directed trains running in the correct direction into the correct platform. Position colour-light signals indicated to the driver that this was the case. On leaving a crossing place on the correct line, the points would be in the trailing position, enabling the train to push safely through the blades. Once the train had cleared the blades, a hydro-pneumatic mechanism returned them to their normal position. All traditional semaphore signals were dispensed with, leading to the reappearance after some 100 years of the fixed board signal. Instead of the distant semaphore, a reflective board displaying an image of a yellow semaphore arm was substituted, and to replace the home and starting signals, square reflective 'end of section' and 'start of section' boards were provided. Every distant board was accompanied by an AWS ramp. Because the siren would be activated by trains travelling in both the right and wrong directions, another board was erected beyond the ramp, to remind drivers travelling away from the distant (in the 'wrong' direction) that the siren did not apply to them.

Radio Electronic Token Block

The most cost-effective solution to single line control to date has been achieved with solid-state (computer) technology. This new system will very soon lead to the disappearance of token working on the national network (though it will remain in operation on preserved lines).

The genesis for Radio Electronic Token Block working came in January 1978, when a severe snow blizzard in Scotland brought down 40 miles of telegraph wires between Wick and Inverness. The cost of replacing the wires was considerably more than that of establishing a radio link and so, in August 1980, token working by transmitting signalling codes by radio was brought into use. Development of Radio Electronic Token Block then followed and Westinghouse received the order at the end of 1983 to make and supply the radio-control equipment and the new signalling panel for installation at the former HR station at Dingwall.

Contrary to what might be assumed, RETB is not simply a matter of a signalman telling a driver over the radio that he can occupy a stretch of single line. The system is based very firmly on the principle that once one driver has permission to enter a single line section, no other train in either direction is allowed in that section. In effect, the only difference between traditional and electronic token block working is that a driver does not physically have a token, staff or tablet in his cab. All other safeguards remain, achieved electronically rather than electro-mechanically.

On the approach to a station, a board tells the driver which radio frequency to select. After stopping his train, he contacts the signalman by radio on this frequency, giving the unique number of his radio equipment. The signalman keys this number and the station at which the train has stopped into his equipment, and only when it has established a link and verified it is communicating with the right train, can the driver then ask permission to enter the single line. The solid-state equipment in the signalbox checks that no other train is on that stretch of line and, after the signalman has pressed the token issue key and the driver has pressed his receive button, it issues an electronic token. The train's unique radio code is then displayed on the signalman's VDU and the same information is printed out on an adjacent computer printer. In the driver's cab, instead of him having a metal token, staff or tablet, the driver receives an illuminated display with the names of the stations or loops either end of the token section, the equivalent of the names which would have appeared on an actual token, staff or tablet. Confirming to the signalman that the display is indicating correctly, the driver is then given permission to leave the station. He contacts the signalman again when he passes another board positioned at the traditional clearing point beyond the station. On receiving this information, the signalman presses a clearance key and the train's radio identity number is then displayed in the relevant section of track on the VDU. After this, the signalman can accept another train in rear, but the RETB equipment prevents him from issuing another token for the same section that the train is travelling on, until it has arrived at the other end of the section. Once there, the driver contacts the signalbox again, the equipment checks that it is communicating with the correct train, and, if so, cancels the electronic token. The board signals and the procedures for AWS remain the same in RETB as for No Signalman Key Token working mentioned above.

The first RETB installation came into use between Dingwall and Kyle of Lochalsh on 6 July 1984 for a trial period, at the same time as the first solid-state interlocking on double track was under test at Leamington Spa. Once proved, RETB was gradually extended and by 1988 Inverness signalling centre was controlling trains through Dingwall to Kyle of Lochalsh, Wick and Thurso, and a new signalling centre at Banavie was controlling trains over the West Highland line to Fort William. RETB was also brought into use in Suffolk between Westerfield (Ipswich) and Oulton Broad North, just outside Lowestoft, in February 1986, and in Wales between Sutton Bridge Junction, Shrewsbury, and Machynlleth in 1988.

Left (206):
Radio Electronic Token Block at Saxmundham signalbox, 29 July 1992. *Brian Morrison*

The majority of this illustrated history has been concerned with fixed signals at the lineside, the mechanisms to operate them, the electrical equipment designed specially for communicating between signalboxes and the men who worked the equipment. This is not an artificial bias but one which reflects the priorities of signal engineers over the last 150 years. Despite the increasing sophistication of equipment, it has only been comparatively recently that the aspects of lineside signals have had a physical effect on the progress of a train.

The development of interlocking in the 1860s was a means to prevent signalmen making mistakes, forcing them to pull levers in the right order and preventing them from setting up routes that would lead to one train colliding with another. The development of lock & block systems followed, to ensure that block instruments were operated correctly, and devices such as Sykes signal reversers (where they were installed) meant that signals were always returned to danger after a train had passed, whether or not a signalman pushed the appropriate lever back to its normal position in the lever frame. Track circuits helped prevent stationary trains being forgotten and when linked to block instruments and lever locks stopped a signalman giving a 'line clear' and clearing his signals when the line was in fact not clear.

But no matter how simple or sophisticated all this equipment was, throughout the 19th century and for many decades of the following one, there was nothing to prevent a driver wilfully ignoring signals and running on into occupied block sections, or over junctions at too high a speed. For perhaps too long, the fear of complacency brought about by too much reliance on mechanical and electrical aids hampered the development of any form of automatic train control. Ever since railway engine drivers were first entrusted with trains of wagons or passenger carriages, there has been a firmly held prejudice against reducing the direct control they had over their locomotive. When the first fixed signals were erected in the 1830s, there was a fear that drivers would become less vigilant and rely too much on the judgement of others — ie railway policemen. This belief survived the introduction of the block system and continued to hinder any attempts to develop physical or electrical links between lineside signals and locomotive controls until the 1890s.

There was no lack of inventions, just a lack of faith in the concept. As early as 1840 the locomotive engineer Edward Bury had experimented with a system on the London & Birmingham Railway, whereby if a signal was at danger, a lever at track level came into contact with an arm on the locomotive, which sounded the locomotive whistle and turned a red lamp in front of the driver. In the 1850s and 60s there were a number of patents for lineside signals operated by passing trains, and for mechanisms to sound the whistle of a locomotive if it overran a signal in the 'on' position. C. F. Whitworth's patent of 1858 (No 751) was just one in a year when Lt Col Yolland of the Railway Inspectorate recommended the use of devices capable of applying a train's brake automatically if it passed a signal at danger.

But it was years before locomotives were actually provided with brakes at all, and consequently until these became standard from the late 1880s onwards, what few experiments that were carried out were concentrated on giving drivers an audible indication in the cab of the aspect of the signal they were passing. There was some debate as to whether the indication of both stop and distant signals should be repeated, but most developments concentrated on the latter.

Audible Signals

With the spread of the block system in the 1870s, the distant signal's function became a means of indicating to drivers whether or not all the stop signals they were approaching were in the all clear or danger position. If the distant was on, a driver would begin to slow his train, and in the years before the introduction of locomotive and automatic continuous brakes, this meant he would sound the engine whistle, to alert his guard to apply his brake. So important did the indication of the distant become, that during fog and falling snow a man had to be positioned at every distant to place detonators on the line if it was in the 'on' position.

The role of the fogman changed very little before the introduction of colour-light signals in the 1920s and 1930s, but there were various improvements as to the means by which detonators were placed on the track. In 1865, Joseph Rowe had patented (No 1880) a mechanism for keeping a detonator permanently on the track if the auxiliary signal showed danger and removing it automatically when the signal was pulled off. By the end of the century, at busy locations and those prone to frequent fogs, some fogmen were put in charge of equipment that was capable of holding a number of detonators attached to mechanisms that could remove spent cartridges and replace them with new ones. Where detonators had to be used in emergencies, a number of railway companies installed detonator placers operated from levers or stirrups in the signalbox. By the Grouping of 1923, the GWR calculated it had 2,204 levers working such equipment, making it a common feature of that company's signalboxes.

The next logical step was to replace the detonator with a device that would transmit any audible signal generated at the distant

Right (207):
The Strowger-Hudd warning hooter as fitted experimentally into the cab of an SR locomotive in 1931. If the signal being approached was off, only a short blast was sounded. If the signal was on, the hooter continued to sound until the brakes were automatically applied or the driver reset the equipment with the device above the hooter.
Modern Transport

Left (208):
Official photograph of the last ATC ramp being installed by the GWR on 9 November 1939 at Penzance, completing the protection of '...2,852 miles of its main lines between Paddington and Penzance, Fishguard and Chester'. The caption continued, '...the scheme has cost £250,000 and has necessitated the fitting of 3,250 engines and installing 2,144 ramps to the track'. *GWR*

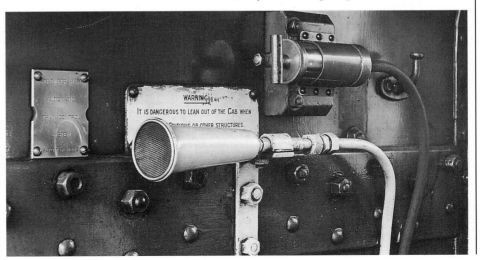

Left (209):
A gantry of the GWR's standard late 19th century semaphores controlled from English Bridge signalbox, Shrewsbury, photographed on 4 June 1960. On the track beneath the only distant signal, and just about to be run over by the departing GWR 'Hall' class locomotive, is the ATC ramp. *Colin P. Walker*

Right (210):
'A4' No 60007 *Sir Nigel Gresley* fitted with BR's standard ATC (AWS) equipment, posed for this official photograph over the two-magnet ramp in the 'four foot' (between the rails). *BR*

signal in fog or falling snow into the locomotive cab. This would dispense with the need for fogmen (and the risks that were part of the job) but it would increase expenditure because of the need to install lineside apparatus and equip all locomotives to receive the signal.

One of the earliest audible cab signalling systems was patented by R. Burns in 1872 (No 440), whereby a gong was sounded beneath the engine footplate if a signal was passed at danger. The patent mentioned that in clear weather the device could be disconnected. There were many other inventions, but the only one that appears to have been put into regular use was patented by the NER's Locomotive Engineer Vincent Raven in 1895 (No 23384). By 1908 over 100 miles of track had been equipped and more than 100 locomotives fitted with apparatus.

Automatic Train Control

By then, there was still no common agreement as to whether or not an audible signal should be supplemented with a partial or complete automatic brake application. In 1873, C. Davidson and C. D. Williams had patented (No 3286) a most comprehensive system, which not only sounded the locomotive's whistle if a signal was at danger, but also automatically shut off steam, applied the engine brake and sounded a gong in the guard's van. As far as is known, the system was never put to any practical use. But as the speed of trains increased in the first decade of the 20th century, the dangers of overrunning signals began to worry railway managers. Inevitably a steady flow of patents began to appear, but apparently only one system progressed beyond the experimental stage.

In 1905, two patents were taken out by employees of the GWR (C. M. Jacobs, R. J. Insell, E. F. Newton and E. A. Bowden — 1905 No 12661, and Insell and Jacobs — 1905 No 25955) for an audible cab system with provision for an automatic brake application. As with all other previous mechanisms, it relied on an arm on the locomotive coming into physical contact with a lineside device, in this case a ramp set between the rails. But the GWR system was

superior to others, because it gave a driver an audible indication whether the distant signal was on or off. When the distant signal was off, a bell rang in the cab, and when the distant was on, a whistle sounded. The system was first installed in January 1906 on the Twyford to Henley branch.

Later that year, in July 1906, a high speed derailment at Salisbury resulted in 24 fatalities, and only two months later a GNR express inexplicably ran through Grantham station with all the signals at danger, coming to grief at the junction to the north of the station, killing 14 people. Neither of these accidents could have been prevented if the brakes had been applied automatically at the distant signals but the results might not have been so severe if they had. The accidents shocked everyone, and the GWR's reaction was immediately to transform its audible system into a full 'automatic train control' (ATC) system. The driver could still cancel an audible warning if the distant signal was on (the whistle of the initial system being replaced by a hooter in the new ATC) but if he did not respond in time, a full brake application was automatically triggered.

So confident of their modified system were the GWR engineers that when it was installed on the Fairford branch in December 1906, all the distant signals were eliminated. The accidents of that year had demonstrated that an automatic brake application was desirable but the abolition of the distant signal altogether and its replacement with an automatic cab control was a complete anathema to the majority of signal engineers. C. B. Byles, Signal Engineer of the L&YR, summed up those conservative feelings when in the April 1907 edition of *Railway Gazette* he wrote '…such a revolution of method is entirely out of the question'.

The Fairford experiment was not repeated and cab signalling even today has not replaced physical lineside signals. But the GWR did decide to extend the use of its ATC further. All lines between Reading and Slough were equipped by 1908 and ATC reached Paddington in 1910. Before the outbreak of World War 1, 144 track miles out of London had been fitted with 168 track ramps, and nearly 100 locomotives had ATC apparatus.

Other companies were never as committed as the GWR and various experiments following the accidents of 1906

showed just how undecided they were about the direction cab signalling should take. In 1906 trials of an electro-mechanical version of Vincent Raven's system (patents 1906 Nos 10507 and 14089) were successfully completed, the new equipment intended to give drivers advanced warning of the state of signals for diverging routes, not just the aspects of distant and home signals. In 1908 the NER planned to install this system along its main line between Newcastle and Durham. In the same year the SECR experimented with a system (Bouneviall & Smith) whereby when a locomotive was stopped at a home signal, it made contact with a ramp between the rails, enabling the driver to speak to the signalman by telephone from the cab. In 1911, Dugald Drummond the Chief Mechanical Engineer of the LSWR devised his own variation of the GWR's ATC. Then in 1915, A. F. Bound, one of the few signal engineers who seems to have become actively involved with such systems, along with the Chief Locomotive Draughtsman of the GCR, experimented with their home-grown 'Reliostop' equipment. Unlike other systems, it was designed to work with stop signals as well as distants. Any indication and partial brake application at a distant could be overruled by the driver but if a brake application was triggered by the passing of a stop signal at danger, the driver could not intervene and, if he and his locomotive survived, the equipment could not be reset again until a new piece of dowel was inserted into the apparatus. A similar system devised about the same time by the Sykes Interlocking Co and E. S. Tiddeman of the GER was also triggered at both the distant and stop signals.

As with other innovations, World War 1 put a halt to further debate and development work. In 1920 the new Ministry of Transport, which had assumed the responsibilities of the old Board of Trade, set up a committee to look into automatic train control, but after the Grouping in 1923 every company except the GWR actually made a conscious decision not to develop any form of cab signalling. At the end of 1928, the GWR agreed to extend ATC and by the close of 1933, 2,500 locomotives had been equipped and 2,200 miles of track fitted with ramps.

The other railway companies believed that improving the siting of signals, the replacement of semaphore distants with

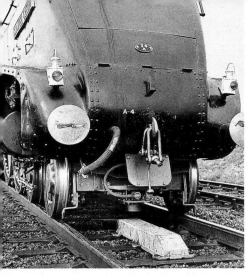

colour-light signals (once their fog-penetrating qualities had been proved) and where possible complete colour-light signalling, rendered any cab signalling unnecessary. By the outbreak of World War 2, the LMS, LNER and SR had all experimented with the Strowger-Hudd system, which unlike the GWR system worked by magnetic induction, not by the physical contact of a ramp in the track with an arm under the cab (Picture 207). But they were still unconvinced, despite a number of accidents that could have been prevented if some form of automatic brake application equipment had been in use. Alone among the Big Four only the GWR was convinced of the benefits of ATC and by the end of the 1930s had succeeded in equipping almost all its locomotive fleet and main lines with ATC apparatus (Pictures 208 & 209).

Once again a world war proved a convenient excuse for shelving any plans the LMS, LNER and SR might have had for ATC, and by nationalisation in 1948 only the LMS had made any further progress, having installed Strowger-Hudd equipment along the former London, Tilbury & Southend Railway.

A New Standard

With nationalisation came a new optimism for the revitalisation of the railway network, rundown to a state of near collapse by the demands put upon it during the war. In 1951, a committee of the Railway Executive was set up to develop a new standard ATC for British Railways. By then, the progressive view was that a visual indication in the cab should supplement the audible one. Initially this was resisted, as the GWR's ATC equipment had proved successful in service without such an indication, but this additional feature was very soon incorporated into the experiments.

The first of these were carried out between New Barnet and Huntingdon on the former GN main line, using modified GW cab apparatus working with Strowger-Hudd equipment that had been purchased for use on the line between Glasgow Queen Street and Edinburgh. The aim was to achieve the same standard of reliability as the GWR system without the locomotive having to make physical contact with the track ramp. The mix of equipment was soon found to be an

unsatisfactory one, and so completely new equipment was fabricated. Trials of the new apparatus took place between King's Cross and Grantham and in May 1956 the Minister of Transport gave his approval for the manufacture of this new equipment, which was to become British Railways' standard ATC.

It has to be questioned whether the wait for the development of new equipment was actually justified, given that all ex-GWR lines and locomotives were protected by a system that had been in operation daily since the 1930s and had so obviously proved its reliability beyond all doubt.

ATC to AWS

The track equipment of the new BR standard ATC consisted of two magnets laid between the rails approximately 200yd in rear of a distant signal, whether semaphore or colour-light (Picture 210). The approach magnet was a permanent one, while the second was an electromagnet. When the distant signal was off, current flowed through the electromagnet contrary to the permanent magnet, causing a bell to ring in the locomotive cab. If the distant was on, the current did not flow and the permanent magnet caused a horn to sound in the cab. If the driver took no action within two or three seconds to cancel the warning and start to apply the ordinary brakes, the vacuum in the braking system was destroyed within the next 13-15sec to bring the train to a stand. On cancelling the horn with the resetting lever, the aspect of a visual indicator changed from black to black and yellow strips and this indication could not be altered until the next clear signal was passed. If the distant signal was off, the sequence outlined above was still triggered by the passing of the permanent magnet, but before the horn had time to sound it was negated by the current flowing through the electromagnet, causing the bell to sound in the cab. As with any other piece of signalling equipment, the ATC was designed to be fail-safe; in other words, if for whatever reason the electromagnet was not energised (ie it failed), a negative — ie safe — indication was transmitted to the driver.

In February 1958, J. H. Currey, Signal & Communications Development Engineer of British Railways Central Staff, read a paper to the Institution of Railway Signal Engineers, giving a detailed account of the new standard ATC. An important part of the new standard system was that on lines controlled by multi-aspect colour-light signals, ATC was to be installed at all signals, giving warnings at yellows, double yellows and reds. It was announced that an order for 2,000 sets of track equipment, and apparatus for 2,000 locomotives had been ordered, to be used to extend the existing coverage between King's Cross and Grantham, northwards to York, to equip the lines between Euston and Blisworth, and Edinburgh and Glasgow.

In 1959 ATC was renamed AWS — Advanced Warning System — and by the following year the first significant installations of the new equipment were being

brought into use. On 6 March 1960 the Southern Region's first installation was commissioned on the Salisbury-Exeter main line as the first stage of three five-year programmes to equip all the Region's lines. The Region's aim was to install AWS in areas still controlled by semaphore signals, before turning its attention to lines with colour-light signals.

By the summer of 1960 AWS had been completed on all tracks between King's Cross and Newcastle, between Edinburgh and Burnmouth, on the ex-LNER lines between Edinburgh and Glasgow and on the West Coast main line between Euston and Stafford. Until the electrification of the ex-LTSR, modifications were made to the existing Strowger-Hudd track equipment to enable locomotives fitted with the new standard AWS apparatus to operate over the line. On 18 November 1960 AWS was brought into operation between Salisbury and Worting Junction on the Southern Region, and according to official statistics, by the end of the year nearly 600 route miles had been equipped and almost 2,000 locomotives fitted with the new apparatus.

The following year, 1961, BR claimed that nearly 1,000 route miles had been equipped with AWS, boosting the total to 2,346 route miles with just under five and a half thousand locomotives fitted. Early in 1963 installation was completed on the West Coast main line between Euston and Carlisle, and with the commissioning of AWS between Newcastle and Alnmouth at the same time, the whole of the East Coast main line between King's Cross and Edinburgh was equipped.

AWS was originally designed for vacuum-fitted motive power, but by the summer of 1963 Southern Region engineers had successfully adapted the system for its air-braked electric and diesel multiple-units. When AWS was commissioned between Surbiton and Woking on 2 August 1963, the Southern Region could boast that it had complete coverage from Waterloo to Exeter and Bournemouth West. But this was the prelude to one of the more bizarre episodes in British Railways' signalling history.

After January 1963, Southern Region lines west of Salisbury were transferred to the Western Region and because that Region's 'Warship' diesels were still fitted with ex-GWR ATC equipment, neither system was able to operate. At first the Western Region tackled this anomaly by removing the standard AWS equipment, only changing its approach five years later when much of the Salisbury-Exeter line had been singled, deciding then that its diesel fleet would be dual fitted for both ATC and AWS operation.

The problem of the phasing out and replacing the ex-GWR ATC system continued into the 1970s. When Saltley powerbox was opened in 1969, there were still enough locomotives fitted with ATC equipment to justify the fitting of the appropriate GWR ramps at certain new colour-light signals. It was not until 1976 that the very last ex-GWR ATC equipment was removed from the Hereford area, and the conversion to the standard BR system was complete.

10 Level Crossings

Gates

One of the earliest pieces of railway legislation was concerned with places where public roads crossed railways on the level. The Railway Level Crossings Act of 1839 stipulated that at such places, railway companies had to provide gates under the control of gate keepers (*Picture 211*). Three years later the Regulation of Railways Act reinforced this requirement, adding that gates should normally be closed across the road and opened only when necessary. The Board of Trade had the power to make exemptions and over the years the stipulation was relaxed but nevertheless, as late as 1910, C. B. Byles commented in his *The First Principles of Railway Signalling* that, '...the public have no legal ground of complaint if they are kept waiting while the gates are opened for them to pass through'.

In 1845 clauses relating to level crossings, along with other miscellaneous legal requirements, were brought together in the Railways Clauses Act, and a further stipulation was added that where turnpike roads were crossed on the level, the speed of trains at these places should not exceed 4mph. Over the years this particular clause was quietly ignored, but before it became obsolete, Warwickshire County Council at the very end of the 19th century found it a useful stick with which to beat the LNWR. At Atherstone the railway crossed Watling Street, the main London to Chester road (later the A5), on the level. The County Council, having had little success in its attempt to persuade the railway company to build a bridge to replace the crossing, discovered that the Trent Valley Act of 1845, which authorised the railway through the town, contained the turnpike clause. It obtained an injunction against the railway, compelling it to honour its own Act and run its trains over the level crossing at no more than 4mph, and although the LNWR challenged this in the courts, the injunction was upheld. The County Council ploy proved successful and a replacement bridge was opened to road traffic in September 1903.

By then county councils, having taken control of road maintenance under the Local Government Act of 1888, were trying to improve local highways, both as a response to the demands of private car owners and firms operating new lorries, and as a way of encouraging more road usage. Yet as the roads improved and the internal combustion engine began to make its mark, the thousands of traditional railway level crossings up and down the country continued to be protected by pitch pine white gates and simple red lamps, as they had been since the 1840s and would continue to be so for at least another 50 years.

One of the earliest references to the red gate lamp was in 1843, when General Pasley commented on the level crossings of the Northern & Eastern Railway (later part of the GER) between Stratford and Bishop's Stortford. He wrote:

'The trains...never slacken their speed on passing those points, unless the gates should be shut across the railway, which are sufficiently conspicuous by day, and rendered so by a red lamp at night, which is a signal to stop.'

Where rail traffic was frequent, or where shunting took place over level crossings, there was often not enough time between trains for gate keepers to open and shut gates, and as their loyalty was obviously to the railway, there were complaints about the length of time gates were closed across the road. For example, in December 1855, Nottingham Town Council felt it necessary to set up a committee especially to, '...enquire into the evils of the level crossing over Queen's Road...' As a result, the Board of Trade used its powers to order the MR to keep the gates normally closed across the railway, and in 1857 the railway company installed 'self-acting' gates to speed up the opening and closing process. Other town councils had similar problems and in 1863 the Railway Clauses Act specifically prevented trains from standing on or being shunted over level crossings.

The 'self-acting' mechanism referred to was undoubtedly one which allowed all four gates to be opened and closed simultaneously, and in the following decades railway companies and most signalling contractors began to develop and manufacture such equipment. Where signalboxes were built next to level crossings, the gate mechanism was often operated from a wheel in the box, every company, needless to say, preferring its own particular and often peculiar design (*Pictures 212 & 213*). The signalling contractors McKenzie & Holland and the GWR, for example, actually produced some frames which incorporated gate wheels.

In block working, signalmen could accept trains even when crossing gates were closed across the tracks but the interlocking prevented them pulling their signals off until the gates were secured against road traffic. Various mechanisms prevented the gates from moving once opened or closed, this usually taking the form of a vertical cast-iron plate in the roadway which engaged with an extension of the outermost wooden member of the gate. When the gates were closed across the railway, the gate-stops remained flush with the road surface, rising automatically when the gates were swung open.

Where gates were controlled from signalboxes, they had to be closed to road traffic well in advance of the arrival of the train so that its progress was not checked at the distant signal. Consequently, on important and busy roads, wicket gates were usually provided for pedestrians, which could remain unlocked after the main gates had been closed. Levers in the main frame, or sometimes in a separate frame, could then be used to lock the wicket gates just before the train arrived.

Where public level crossings were not controlled directly from signalboxes, crossing keepers were usually provided with an instrument which repeated the indications of the block instruments of the adjacent signalboxes (*Picture 214*). When telephones came into general use in the first part of the 20th century, some crossings were provided with telephone links to neighbouring signalboxes. Some railway companies erected distant signals either side of crossings, worked from a ground frame. The distant signals remained off while the crossing gates were closed to road traffic, and were only returned to the 'on' position if the crossing keeper had to close the gates over the railway. The use of distant signals in this way was still part of the Ministry of Transport Requirements of 1950.

The fact that such requirements for level crossing protection had not altered for nearly 100 years illustrates how few technological innovations there had been in that time. There were a few experiments with power-operated gates, but they remained isolated developments. For example, in 1907 the L&YR installed a 2hp electric motor to operate the level crossing gates at Waterloo, near Liverpool. The operating lever stood normally midway in the frame. When pushed it drove the motor in one direction and when pulled, in the opposite direction. It was claimed the gates could be opened or closed in just 15sec, the signalman being able to regulate the speed. In 1925 the LNER installed electrically-operated gates at High Street, Lincoln, which remained in use until replaced by lifting barriers in the 1990s.

Lifting Barriers

Although the interwar years witnessed many innovations, the traditional gated level crossing remained as the Victorian engineers had designed it. Considering the financial implications of manning thousands of gated public road level crossings throughout the country, it is surprising how long it took before changes were made (*Picture 215*). The 1839/1845 Act remained in force until 1954, when BR was finally given permission to substitute lifting barriers for gates, although the obligation to provide on the spot supervision remained (*Picture 216*). Three

years later a Ministry of Transport and British Transport Commission working party report, following visits to a number of continental barrier installations, led to a further Act allowing for the automatic activation of lifting barriers by track circuits or by remote control, removing the need for gate keepers at every crossing.

Crossings with automatic lifting barriers, or no form of physical barrier at all, had long been a feature on the Continent and in America. Economically, their use in this country was inevitable. But almost as soon as they were introduced, their use was controversial, and their misuse, which was the cause of a number of serious accidents, led to several inquiries from which emerged more recommendations for improved safety measures at level crossings than in the previous 120 years.

In 1960 new standards for road signs and flashing lights at barrier crossings were incorporated into the Ministry of Transport's Requirements. It was recommended that two red lights lettered STOP, mounted side by side, should flash before the barriers descended and continue to flash until the barriers began to rise after the passage of the train. If the barriers stayed down to allow another train to pass, then an additional illuminated sign should display SECOND TRAIN COMING.

One of the first installations conforming to the new requirements was brought into use by the Eastern Region at Ware during the summer of 1960. The four barriers were controlled from the new signalbox there. Each barrier was 28ft long, painted in red and white with suspended fringes or 'skirts' to prevent animals or children running under the barriers in the down position. On the signalman pressing one of two buttons, two flashing lights warned motorists that the barriers were about to fall. After five seconds the left-hand barriers descended and once in position were followed by the right-hand ones.

Experiments with the control of a level crossing with full barriers by closed-circuit television (cctv) from Kings Dyke signalbox near Peterborough led during 1971 to the Department of the Environment approving further installations. Throughout the 1970s the use of full barriers, operated either directly or monitored by cctv from signalboxes or powerboxes, became commonplace. Between 1975 and 1985, the number of level crossings protected with gates fell from 1,269 to 576, and the number of those protected by full barriers operated directly by signalmen rose from 394 to 583 in the same period.

Automatic Half-Barrier Crossings (ahb)

Strictly speaking, crossings of this type do not form part of the signalling system. From their first use on BR, it was always the intention that their operation should be controlled by the approach of a train and not by the aspect of the signals. Whether the barriers were raised, lowered or had failed, their position was not interlocked in any way with the signals. Any failures were detected in the nearest signalbox, from where train drivers could be warned of the situation.

In February 1961 the first automatic half barriers operated by the approach of a train were installed at Spath, just outside Uttoxeter. On the train occupying the track circuit in rear of the crossing as well as activating a treadle, twin red lights began to flash accompanied by a two-tone gong. After 8sec the barriers began to descend, the aim being to have them in position at least 5sec before the train passed over the level crossing. Once the barriers were down the gong ceased to sound. A 'second train approaching' warning was provided and the half barriers were designed to snap if they were rammed by a trapped vehicle.

Modifications of the basic design followed and by 1964 a standard design had been approved. In July that year, standard automatic half barriers were installed at Manea, Waterbeach, Egginton, Castle Ashby, Naworth, Pelaw, Dumfries, Cooksbridge, Wokingham, Kidlington, and Wellington on the Taunton-Exeter line. A film explaining the operation of the barriers was made to show at local schools, and posters and leaflets were also distributed.

But the introduction of the new ahbs was controversial and the terrible accident at Hixon crossing between Stone and Colwich on 6 January 1968 seemed to confirm the public's worst fears. On that day, a Manchester-Euston express crashed into a transporter lorry trailer straddling the tracks at the automatic half barrier crossing. The barriers had lowered automatically as the train approached, before the trailer was clear of the crossing. The driver, second man, spare driver and eight passengers were killed. As a result a public inquiry was set up under the chairmanship of E. B. Gibbens, QC. The official report published in August 1968 blamed the driver of the trailer for not contacting the signalman before using the crossing, his employers and the police escort. What emerged from the report was that there was a mistaken belief that while a vehicle was on the crossing, no train could approach. The trailer's owners were heavily criticised for not informing their drivers of the risks and procedures for heavy and slow loads on such crossings, and it appears there was widespread ignorance about all aspects of their operation. It was felt that this was partly due to the Ministry of Transport's reluctance to undertake a national campaign of education, although posters and leaflets had been used in locations where barriers had been installed.

The Report did not condemn the use of automatic half barrier crossings, but it made a number of stringent recommendations, including an extension of the time from 24 to 37sec between the triggering of the first warning lights to the moment the train passed the crossing, the addition of an amber warning light to show a few seconds prior to the red flashing lights, better road profiles and sighting either side of the crossing, the use of yellow markings on the crossings to indicate to motorists that in queuing traffic they must not stop on the crossing, mandatory signs either side of crossings to inform drivers of slow and heavy loads that they had to telephone the adjacent signalman, the withdrawal of the new barrier sign (the traditional gate sign was reintroduced), and heavier penalties for 'zigzagging' round lowered barriers.

The first ahb crossings modified in response to the new recommendations were commissioned during 1970 (Picture 217). To coincide with the changes, two million leaflets were distributed to local authorities and transport organisations all over the country, along with 350,000 posters. All crossings that had to be altered were eligible for a special grant but as the costs of new crossings had risen from between £7,000 and £8,000 to between £13,000 and £20,000, it was this financial consideration that virtually stopped any further new installations until the end of the decade.

What enabled a new start to be made was the publication in 1978 of the Report on Level Crossing Protection, which included a new set of recommendations relaxing many of those in the Hixon Report. But within a year level crossings were back in the news again and receiving yet more bad press. Since the 1830s there had always been occupation crossings, where users opened and closed the gates themselves. The gates swung away from the railway so they posed no obstruction to rail traffic if left open. During the 1960s and 1970s, a number of user-operated barrier crossings were installed instead of gates but their safety came in for much criticism following an accident at Naas level crossing near Lydney on 1 March 1979. The subsequent report recommended that such crossings should be converted to 'automatic open crossings remotely monitored' (AOCR — see below). The Minister of Transport confirmed in October 1979 that he had accepted the main conclusion of the 'Level Crossing Protection' report of that year, and the level crossing at Naas became the first to receive the new design of warning signs and lights in the summer of 1983.

Open Crossings

The open crossing was, of course, the ultimate cost-effective level crossing, one devoid of any form of physical barrier and one which remains the most controversial aspect of the modern railway. If ahb crossings were an incentive for some car drivers to try their racing and rallying skills to 'beat the barriers', then open crossings were open invitations for the suicidal.

At automatic open crossings (AOCs), flashing lights warn road users of the approach of a train, and in some places (at automatic open crossings locally monitored — AOCL) the train driver is made aware he is approaching an open crossing by the display of a flashing white light. If that light does not flash or is extinguished, he is instructed to stop. At these crossings and those remotely monitored (AOCR) where no white light is provided, the failure of the road traffic signals is detected in the nearest signalbox.

Among the first open level crossings were those at Forden on the Shrewsbury-Aberystwyth line, and at Blackgrange on the Stirling to Alloa line, the crossing opening on 24 June 1973. By 1986 there were 206 automatic open crossings locally monitored and 44 automatic open crossings remotely monitored, with many more planned. Then on 26 July 1986, 10 people were killed and 51 injured when a Bridlington to Hull train hit a van on an open crossing at Lockington between Hutton Cranswick and Arram, which led to the immediate suspension of all further installations (the next in line for alteration were those on the ex-GNR branch to Skegness).

Yet another inquiry followed under intense media scrutiny and yet more recommendations were made. Pessimistically, Prof Stott remarked that he thought no alterations at open and ahb crossings would improve their safety record, because most accidents were attributable to the behaviour of road users, and that was something he believed even education could not change. The problems of level crossing safety have obviously not yet been solved.

Below (217):
The ahb crossing at Ripe, Sussex, was one of the first to be modified to conform with the new standards recommended in the Hixon Crossing report. The additional amber light and illuminated 'ANOTHER TRAIN COMING' display are very obvious, as are the more prominent road markings. *BR*

Glossary

This glossary does not provide a definition of every technical term used in this book. Sometimes a term is explained within the main text, and then the reader can look up that term in the index, the first page reference to it usually containing the explanation. The definitions given here are not definitive either but are worded in as precise but simple a language as is possible. Words which appear in **bold** within the explanatory text below are themselves explained elsewhere in this glossary.

all-electric power signalling
A phrase usually confined to the period 1890-1918 to describe the moving of **points** and signals by electrical means.

aspect, signal
The indication of a signal, mainly used in reference to colour-light signals.

atmospheric traction
An experiment of the 1840s, whereby an extension fitted beneath a carriage of a train was slotted into a cast-iron tube laid between the rails so that when the air was sucked out of the tube, in front of the extension, the atmospheric pressure behind it pushed the carriage attached to it, forward.

back-light
In the back of a semaphore signal lamp, opposite the main lens, was a small glazed opening allowing the flame from the lamp to be seen when the signal was in the **on** position and obscured when the signal was pulled **off.**

back-lock
A means of preventing a lever or switch, after it had been moved from its initial unlocked position, from being moved/operated again until further mechanical or electrical locking had **proved** it was safe to do so.

berth track circuit
A **track circuit** on the approach side of (**in rear of**) a signal.

bi-directional running
In normal circumstances, on stretches of double track, each line was used only by trains travelling in the same direction, but if those tracks are signalled for bi-directional running, then in emergencies either line can be used by trains travelling in opposite directions (the signals controlling conflicting moves on the same line being fully **interlocked**, of course).

block instrument
An electrical device for exchanging and displaying messages between signalmen when working the block system; most **block instruments** were based around the circuitry of the Cooke & Wheatstone single needle telegraph instrument, although other electrical engineers, notably Edward Tyer, popularised varieties using induced current needles or miniature semaphores; a **single-stroke bell** can also be classed as a **block instrument**, and a number of instruments incorporated needles (or miniature semaphores) and bells.

block section
The section of track from the most **advanced** stop signal (the furthest stop signal away from a signalbox in the direction of travel of the train) of one signalbox to the first stop signal of the next signalbox **in advance of** it.

booking lad
Someone employed in a signalbox to keep the train register up to date and operate the **speaking telegraph instruments** and/or telephones.

break-section signalbox
A signalbox controlling only signals built especially to divide what would otherwise have been a long section between two signalboxes, and creating an additional **block section.**

calling-on signal
Usually placed under a stop signal and, when operated, would indicate to a train driver to move his train (or engine) carefully forward (past the main signal at danger) to either a predetermined location, or to the adjacent signalbox from where he would await further instructions.

catch handle
Part of a metal lever usually fixed behind the top part of that lever which operated a metal bar at the back of the lever and was connected to a metal block which kept the lever either in its **normal** or **reversed** position in a **lever frame.**

check-lock
An intermediate position in the **stroke** of a lever (usually a miniature one) from which it could not be physically moved any further until a 'check' had been made electrically (**proving**) that locks and other pieces of equipment had responded correctly to the initial movement of the lever.

clearing point (overlap)
A set distance beyond (**in advance of**) a signal (originally a stop signal) that had to be unobstructed before the **aspect** of that signal could be altered from red (danger) to a less restricted one (eg green).

commissioned
Brought into use.

commutator
A component part of a **block instrument** which, when manipulated by a signalman, altered the indication ('line clear', 'train on line', 'line blocked' [normal] of that instrument).

compensator
A mechanical device fitted into a long run of point rodding to compensate for the effects of expansion and contraction caused by a change in temperature.

detector
A mechanism to ensure that a signal could not be altered to the **off** position unless point blades were in their correct position.

detonator
A small charge of explosive contained in a flat circular metal 'cap' (current examples approximately 50cm in diameter) attached to two soft metal straps that could be used to clip the detonator to the top of the rail — the detonator would explode when the wheel of a train squashed the cap.

electro-pneumatic
Compressed air as a means of power controlled by an electrical device.

facing point
If a **point** could turn a train onto another line in the same direction as that train was travelling, the **point** was (and is) described as facing (if a train has to stop and reverse over a **point**, that **point** was [and is] described as 'trailing').

fail-safe
Used to describe a piece of equipment that was (and is) designed to prevent any further danger occurring if it malfunctioned — eg, if a signal wire broke, the semaphore arm would return to or remain at danger.

fixed-formation
A train consisting of carriages or wagons usually permanently coupled together.

fixed signal
A mid-19th century definition of any signal attached to a post set in, or fixed to, the ground (as opposed to a signal given by a man holding a flag or lamp).

flat crossing
Where two or more tracks cross each other on the level.

fouling bar
A mechanism to stop a signal on an adjacent line being altered to all clear (**off**) if by passing that signal a train was likely to collide with another on the line fitted with the fouling bar.

fringe signalbox (fringe box)
A term used from the 1960s to describe an existing signalbox (usually mechanical) that controlled trains entering or leaving an area controlled by a **powerbox**.

ground frame
A **lever frame** usually installed in the open at track level to control a few **points** and signals, the frame not having the full status nor full control of trains as a signalbox or **powerbox**; the operation of **ground frames** was often controlled from adjacent signalboxes.

ground signal
A loose term for shunting signals, most of which were installed at track level.

headway
The distance between two trains travelling in the same direction on the same stretch of track.

hot-box detector
A device for alerting signalmen that the axle-boxes of vehicles in a passing train were overheating.

illuminated diagram
A coloured plan of the tracks and signals under the control of a signalbox or **powerbox** installed in that signalbox or **powerbox**, the presence of trains on those tracks being indicated by small electric lamps set into the plan.

in advance of
From a signalman's point of view, used to describe any line on which a train was travelling away from him; when used in reference to a signal, the section of track beyond a signal (that section usually controlled by that signal).

in rear of
From a signalman's point of view, used to describe any line on which a train was approaching him; when used in reference to a signal, the section of track in front of a signal (on the 'approach side').

interlocking
The means (mechanical or electrical) of connecting the devices (eg levers, switches, etc) controlling the movement of signals and **points** so as to co-ordinate the movements of those devices and prevent trains colliding.

Intermediate Block Signals (IBSs)
Signals that created an additional **block section** between signalboxes and were controlled from the signalbox **in rear of** them.

lever frame
A number of levers fitted together into a cast-iron and wrought-iron frame and **interlocked** with each other; (a frame consisted of various component parts — see *A Guide to Mechanical Locking Frames*, Signalling Study Group, 1989 [available via the Signalling Record Society]).

lever tail
An extension at the base of a lever opposite its pivot (or fulcrum) onto which the rods, wires or chains that led to the **points** and **fixed signals** were connected.

locking tray
Between 1860 and 1890 there were various ways of achieving the **interlocking** between levers and, strictly speaking, **locking trays** were only used in **tappet locking** to guide the flat metal bars (the tappets), connected to the levers, through the locks held in the tray.

margining
The process of deciding how much time was needed between each train once the sequence of trains (the order in which a number of trains should run) had been decided, and whether a sufficient margin could be found to maintain that sequence.

normal/reverse
Used to describe the relative position of any piece of equipment but usually signals and points; normal = the usual (normal) position of a piece of equipment, usually **on** in the case of a signal, or in the case of a lever in a **lever frame**, usually upright (or almost upright); reverse = the secondary position — **off** in the case of a signal, or, in the case of a lever, inclined forward towards the signalman.

off (see on and off)

on and off
Used to describe the indication or **aspect** of a signal; on = danger; off = all clear; 'to pull off' meant **reversing** a lever to move a signal to its 'all clear' position.

operating floor (signalbox)
The room within a signalbox containing the **lever frame**, **block instruments**, **train register**, **speaking telegraph instruments**, telephone, and other equipment for working **points** and signals and the **block system**.

overhead signalbox
A signalbox built over the running lines.

plunger
Usually a brass mechanism which when pushed acted as an electrical switch.

point
The means of dividing two tracks.

possession
The temporary closure to passenger and goods traffic of a piece of track for maintenance purposes by the Permanent Way (PW) Department.

power signalling
A phrase coined in the last decades of the 19th century to describe the working of **points** and signals by other than purely mechanical means.

powerbox
A corruption of power-signalbox, used mainly after 1960 to describe signalboxes equipped with panels of switches or buttons capable of controlling **points** and signals spread over a wide geographical area.

proving (to prove, proved)
Making sure by mechanical, electrical or electronic means that a piece of equipment had functioned correctly when a lever, switch, or button in a signalbox or a **track circuit** or **treadle** had been operated.

Railway Mania, The
A period of frantic speculation in new railway schemes all over the country; strictly speaking the years 1845 and 1846, when more railway bills were introduced into Parliament than at any other time in history.

relay
The equivalent of an electrical switch.

relay interlocking
Interlocking achieved by **relays** instead of mechanically.

Requirements
A set of standards (not obligatory) for the construction and operation of a railway, issued periodically from 1858 by the Board of Trade and then, after 1919, by the Ministry of Transport.

reverse (see normal/reverse)

route mile
A unit of measurement for calculating the distance between two places, regardless of the number of lines (tracks); eg 20 route miles of single track was (and is) the same as 20 route miles of quadruple (four lines of) track.

running signals
Signals controlling the movement of trains on all lines except sidings.

scissor crossing
Four **points** connecting two parallel tracks, the lines between each **point** intersecting each other to form a **flat crossing**.

shunting frame
A phrase used from the 1960s to describe signalboxes which no longer controlled the passage of trains directly (eg by the **block system**), because that function had been taken over by a **powerbox**, but which continued to operate **points** and their associated signals for local movements.

signal aspect — see aspect/signal

signal repeater
A device (mechanical or electrical) located in a signalbox to show the signalman what indication or **aspect** a particular signal was showing (either **on** or **off**).

signal reverser
An electro-mechanical piece of equipment for altering the indication (**aspect**) of a signal automatically from **off** to **on** when a train had passed that signal.

signal wire adjuster/tensioner
A mechanism installed on the **operating floor** of a signalbox to enable a signalman to adjust the tension of the wire connecting the lever with the signal and compensate for contraction and expansion in that wire caused by changes of temperature.

single-stroke bell
A box (usually wooden) containing an electro-magnet which, when energised by the pressing of a **plunger** or tapper by a signalman in an adjacent signalbox, attracted a small pivoted hammer towards it, the hammer arranged to hit a metal bell (usually brass) mounted either above or below the electro-magnet; the electrical circuit was arranged so that pressing the **plunger** or tapper caused the hammer to hit the bell only once for each press (a 'plunge').

slotting
Originally a mechanical means of enabling one or more semaphore signals to be controlled by two or more signalmen; with colour-light signals 'slotting' was achieved electrically.

speaking telegraph instrument
The first practical electric telegraph using a centrally-pivoted vertical single needle was patented by Cooke & Wheatstone in 1837, and, because the movement of the needles from side to side was used to spell out letters and/or messages, instruments with just one or two needles were soon being called 'speaking telegraph instruments' (see also **block instrument**).

spectacle
A metal frame containing one, two or three differently coloured glasses which could be moved in front of a signal lamp to alter the **aspect** of that signal.

stroke, lever
The movement of a lever, and the distance of that movement, from **normal** and **reverse**, and **reverse** and **normal**.

subsidiary signal
A non-**running signal** or a signal controlling a restricted movement.

tappet locking
The simplest and, in the 20th century, most popular way of achieving **interlocking** between levers in a **lever frame**; flat metal bars (the tappets) were connected to the levers, and these tappets passed through **locking trays** holding the locks moving at right angles to the tappets, engaging and/or disengaging in slots, notches or ports cut into the tappets.

theatre-type route indicator
A metal box mounted next to a signal (semaphore or colour-light) in which a number, letter or abbreviated word could be displayed; the indication was usually illuminated either by shining a light at or through the number, letter or abbreviated word, or by forming that display with a matrix of small electric light bulbs.

thumb switch
An electrical switch that could be rotated from side to side between the thumb and first finger.

track circuit
A **relay** and battery connected to each other by the rails of an insulated section of track to form an electrical circuit which, when short-circuited by the presence of a train, can form or break another electrical circuit to operate another piece of electrical equipment.

track mile
A unit of measurement for calculating the total mileage of track between two places; eg assuming the **route miles** between two places is 20 miles, then if laid as single track the track mileage is also 20 miles, but if laid as quadruple (four lines of) track, then the track mileage is 80 miles.

train register
A bound book, the pages of which were printed with a number of columns into which was entered the times of every bell code sent and received by a signalman with adjacent signalboxes, the times the signalman came on and off duty, and selected other pieces of information (eg failures of equipment, visit and signature of stationmaster, times of **possession**, etc).

treadle
A mechanical device set next to the rails and activated (usually depressed) by the passage of a train.

unfitted train
A train consisting of vehicles (carriages or goods wagons) not fitted with brakes or fitted with brakes that could not be applied whilst the train was in motion.

Index

Below (218):
Recalling an earlier age, this temporary signalling platform was erected on the MSLR at Annesley in 1895 and used until the permanent signalbox was ready to control the junction of the company's (by then renamed the GCR) new main line to the capital, opened in March 1899. *Leicestershire Museums, Arts & Records Service (Newton Collection TBF3/3)*